HANDS-ON STANDARDS

Photo-Illustrated Lessons for Teaching
with Math Manipulatives

51 Hands-On Activities for
Grades PreK–K

LEARNING
RESOURCES®

VERNON HILLS • KING'S LYNN

ISBN: 978-1-56911-229-8

LER 0850

380 N. Fairway Drive
Vernon Hills, IL 60061
(800) 222-3909

Printed in China.

Contents

Data Analysis and Probability 112

Blackline Masters

Introduction

How can we make sure that children grasp the real meaning behind mathematical concepts instead of just memorizing numbers and repeating them back on tests? How can we help children develop an in-depth mathematical understanding?

Hands-On Standards: Photo-Illustrated Lessons for Teaching with Math Manipulatives (Grades PreK–K) provides teachers with easy-to-access ways to help children "visualize mathematics." This 144-page manual delivers 51 age-appropriate lessons designed to engage teachers and children in meaningful, authentic learning. Each lesson defines the specific concepts and skills that children will be taught and includes step-by-step procedures for children to use in solving a problem that easily links math to their day-to-day lives. Full-color photographs highlight the steps used in hands-on learning. Because it is important to reinforce learning, each lesson provides additional ways to practice the concepts.

Hands-On Standards is divided into five sections—Number and Operations, Geometry, Algebra, Measurement, and Data Analysis and Probability. These sections are based on National Council of Teachers of Mathematics (NCTM) content strands. Each NCTM-focused lesson provides a structured framework for teachers to use manipulatives as tools to move children from the concrete to the abstract so that children can achieve understanding and succeed on standardized tests.

Each lesson in this book uses one of the following manipulatives:

- Attribute Blocks
- Backyard Bugs™
- 1" Color Cubes
- Color Tiles
- Link 'N' Learn® Links

- Pattern Blocks
- Reversible Graph It! Mat
- Snap Cubes®
- Sorting Circles
- Three Bear Family® Counters

Research on the Benefits of Manipulatives

History of Manipulatives

Since ancient times, people of many different civilizations have used physical objects to help them solve everyday math problems. The ancient civilizations of Southwest Asia (the Middle East) used counting boards. These were wooden or clay trays covered with a thin layer of sand. The user would draw symbols in the sand to tally, for example, an account or take an inventory. The ancient Romans modified counting boards to create the world's first abacus. The Chinese abacus, which came into use centuries later, may have been an adaptation of the Roman abacus.

Similar devices were developed in the Americas. The Mayans and the Aztecs both had counting devices that featured corn kernels strung on string or wires that were stretched across a wooden frame. The Incas had their own unique counting tool—knotted strings called *quipu*.

The late 1800s saw the invention of the first true manipulatives—maneuverable objects that appeal to several different senses and are specifically designed for teaching mathematical concepts. Friedrich Froebel, a German educator who started the world's first kindergarten program in 1837, developed different types of objects to help his kindergarteners recognize patterns and appreciate geometric forms found in nature. In the early 1900s, Italian-born educator Maria Montessori further advanced the idea that manipulatives are important in education. She designed many materials to help preschool and elementary-school children discover and learn basic ideas in math and other subjects.

Since the early 1900s, manipulatives have come to be considered essential in teaching mathematics at the elementary-school level. In fact, for decades, the National Council of Teachers of Mathematics (NCTM) has recommended the use of manipulatives in teaching mathematical concepts at all grade levels (Hartshorn and Boren 1990).

Manipulatives and Curriculum Standards

The NCTM calls for manipulatives to be used in teaching a wide variety of topics in mathematics.

- sorting—a premathematical skill that aids in comprehension of patterns and functions
- ordering—a premathematical skill that enhances number sense and other math-related abilities
- distinguishing patterns—the foundation for making mathematical generalizations
- recognizing geometric shapes and understanding relationships among them
- making measurements, using both nonstandard and standard units with application to both two- and three-dimensional objects
- understanding the base-ten system of numbers
- comprehending mathematical operations— addition, subtraction, multiplication, division
- recognizing relationships among mathematical operations
- exploring and describing spatial relationships
- identifying and describing different types of symmetry
- developing and utilizing spatial memory
- learning about and experimenting with transformations
- engaging in problem solving
- representing mathematical ideas in a variety of ways
- connecting different concepts in mathematics
- communicating mathematical ideas effectively

Different states across the nation have also mandated the use of manipulatives for teaching math. These include California, North Carolina, Texas, and Tennessee, among others. In addition, many local school districts mandate or strongly suggest that manipulatives be used in teaching math, especially for the elementary level.

Manipulative use is recommended because it is supported by both learning theory and educational research in the classroom.

Concrete stage	Representational stage	Abstract stage
A mathematical concept is introduced with manipulatives; children explore the concept using the manipulatives in purposeful activity.	A mathematical concept is represented using pictures of some sort to stand for the concrete objects (the manipulatives) of the previous stage; children demonstrate how they can both visualize and communicate the concept at a pictorial level.	Mathematical symbols (numerals, operation signs, etc.) are used to express the concept in symbolic language; children demonstrate their understanding of the mathematical concept using the language of mathematics.

How Learning Theory Supports the Use of Manipulatives

The theory of experiential education revolves around the idea that learning is enhanced when children acquire knowledge through active processes that engage them (Hartshorn and Boren 1990). Manipulatives can be key in providing effective, active, engaging lessons in the teaching of mathematics.

Manipulatives help children learn by allowing them to move from concrete experiences to abstract reasoning (Heddens 1986; Reisman 1982; Ross and Kurtz 1993). This strategy is exemplified by the Concrete-Representational-Abstract (CRA) instructional approach. The three-stage CRA process is summarized above (The Access Center, October 1, 2004).

The use of manipulatives helps children hone their mathematical thinking skills. According to Stein and Bovalino (2001), "Manipulatives can be important tools in helping students to think and reason in more meaningful ways. By giving students concrete ways to compare and operate on quantities, such manipulatives as pattern blocks, tiles, and cubes can contribute to the development of well-grounded, interconnected understandings of mathematical ideas."

To gain a deep understanding of mathematical ideas, children need to be able to integrate and connect a variety of concepts in many different ways. Clements (1999) calls this type of deep understanding "Integrated-Concrete" knowledge. The effective use of manipulatives can help children connect ideas and integrate their knowledge so that they gain a deep understanding of mathematical concepts.

Teachers play a crucial role in helping children use manipulatives successfully, so that they move through the three stages of learning and arrive at a deep understanding of mathematical concepts.

How Research from the Classroom Supports the Use of Manipulatives

Over the past four decades, studies done at all different grade levels and in several different countries indicate that mathematical achievement increases when manipulatives are put to good use (Canny 1984; Clements 1999; Clements and Battista 1990; Dienes 1960; Driscoll 1981; Fennema 1972, 1973; Skemp 1987; Sugiyama 1987; Suydam 1984). Additional research shows that use of manipulatives over the long-term provides more benefits than short-term use does (Sowell 1989).

With long-term use of manipulatives in mathematics, educators have found that children make gains in the following general areas (Heddens 1986; Picciotto 1998; Sebesta and Martin 2004):

- verbalizing mathematical thinking
- discussing mathematical ideas and concepts
- relating real-world situations to mathematical symbolism
- working collaboratively
- thinking divergently to find a variety of ways to solve problems
- expressing problems and solutions using a variety of mathematical symbols
- making presentations
- taking ownership of their learning experiences
- gaining confidence in their abilities to find solutions to mathematical problems

Studies have shown that children using manipulatives in specific mathematical subjects are more likely to achieve success than children who don't have the opportunity to work with manipulatives. The following are some specific areas in which research shows manipulatives are especially helpful:

Counting Some children need to use manipulatives to learn to count (Clements 1999).

Place Value Using manipulatives increases childrens' understanding of place value (Phillips 1989).

Computation Children learning computational skills tend to master and retain these skills more fully when manipulatives are used as part of their instruction (Carroll and Porter 1997).

Problem Solving Using manipulatives has been shown to help children reduce errors and increase their scores on tests that require them to solve problems (Carroll and Porter 1997; Clements 1999; Krach 1998).

Fractions Children who have appropriate manipulatives to help them learn fractions outperform children who rely only on textbooks when tested on these concepts (Jordan, Miller, and Mercer 1998; Sebesta and Martin 2004).

Ratios Children who have appropriate manipulatives to help them learn fractions also have significantly improved achievement when tested on ratios when compared to children who do not have exposure to these manipulatives (Jordan, Miller, and Mercer 1998).

Algebraic Abilities Algebraic abilities include the ability to represent algebraic expressions, to interpret such expressions, to make connections between concepts when solving linear equations, and to communicate algebraic concepts. Research indicates that children who used manipulatives in their mathematics classes have higher algebraic abilities than those who did not use manipulatives (Chappell and Strutchens 2001).

Manipulatives have also been shown to provide a strong foundation for children mastering the following mathematical concepts (The Access Center, October 1, 2004):

- number relations
- measurement
- decimals
- number bases
- percentages
- probability
- statistics

Well-known math educator Marilyn Burns (Burns 2005) considers manipulatives essential for teaching math to children of all levels. She finds that manipulatives help make math concepts accessible to almost all learners, while at the same time offering ample opportunities to challenge children who catch on quickly to the concepts being taught. Research indicates that using manipulatives is especially useful for teaching low achievers, children with learning disabilities, and English language learners (Marsh and Cooke 1996; Ruzic and O'Connell 2001).

Research also indicates that using manipulatives helps improve the environment in math classrooms. When children work with manipulatives and are then given a chance to reflect on their experiences, not only is mathematical learning enhanced, math anxiety is greatly reduced (Cain-Caston 1996; Heuser 2000). Exploring manipulatives, especially in a self-directed manner, provides an exciting classroom environment and promotes in children a positive attitude toward learning (Heuser 1999; Moch 2001). Among the benefits several researchers found for using manipulatives was that they helped make learning fun (Moch 2001; Smith et al. 1999).

Summary

Research from both learning theory and classroom studies shows that using manipulatives to help teach math can positively affect learning. This is true for children at all levels and of all abilities. It is also true for almost every topic covered in elementary-school mathematics curricula. Papert (1980) calls manipulatives "objects to think with." Incorporating manipulatives into mathematics lessons in meaningful ways helps children grasp concepts with greater ease, making teaching most effective.

Reference Citations

The Access Center, http://coe.jmu.edu/mathvidsr/disabilities.htm (October 1, 2004)

Burns, M. (1996). How to make the most of math manipulatives. *Instructor,* accessed at http://teacher.scholastic.com/lessonrepro/lessonplans/instructor/burns.htm.

Cain-Caston, M. (1996). Manipulative queen. *Journal of Instructional Psychology,* 23(4): 270–274.

Canny, M. E. (1984). The relationship of manipulative materials to achievement in three areas of fourth-grade mathematics: Computation, concept development, and problem solving. *Dissertation Abstracts International,* 45A: 775–776.

Carroll, W. M. & Porter, D. (1997). Invented strategies can develop meaningful mathematical procedures. *Teaching Children Mathematics,* 3(7): 370–374.

Chappell, M. F. & Struthens, M. E. (2001). Creating connections: Promoting algebraic thinking with concrete models. *Mathematics Teaching in the Middle School.* Reston, VA: National Council of Teachers of Mathematics.

Clements, D. H. (1999). "Concrete" manipulatives, concrete ideas. *Contemporary Issues in Early Childhood,* 1(1): 45–60.

Clements, D. H. & Battistia, M. T. (1990). Constructive learning and teaching. *The Arithmetic Teacher,* 38: 34–35.

Dienes, Z. P. (1960). *Building up mathematics.* London: Hutchinson Educational.

Driscoll, M. J. (1984). What research says. *The Arithmetic Teacher,* 31: 34–35.

Fennema, E. H. (1972). Models and mathematics. *The Arithmetic Teacher,* 19: 635–640.

———. (1973). Manipulatives in the classroom. *The Arithmetic Teacher,* 20: 350–352.

Hartshorn, R. & Boren, S. (1990). Experiential learning of mathematics: Using manipulatives. *ERIC Clearinghouse on Rural Education and Small Schools.*

Heddens, J. W. (1986). Bridging the gap between the concrete and the abstract. *The Arithmetic Teacher,* 33: 14–17.

———. Improving mathematics teaching by using manipulatives. Kent State University, accessed at www.fed.cubk.edu.hk.

Heuser, D. (1999). Reflections on teacher philosophies and teaching strategies upon children's cognitive structure development—reflection II; Pennsylvania State University, accessed at http://www.ed.psu.edu/CI/Journals/1999AETS/Heuser.rtf

———. (2000). Mathematics class becomes learner centered. *Teaching Children Mathematics,* 6(5): 288–295.

Jordan, L., Miller, M., & Mercer, C. D. (1998). The effects of concrete to semi-concrete to abstract instruction in the acquisition and retention of fraction concepts and skills. *Learning Disabilities: A Multidisciplinary Journal,* 9: 115–122.

Krach, M. (1998). Teaching fractions using manipulatives. *Ohio Council of Teachers of Mathematics,* 37: 16–23.

Maccini, P. & Gagnon, J. A. (2000, January). Best practices for teaching mathematics to secondary students with special needs. *Focus on Exceptional Children,* 32 (5): 11.

Marsh, L. G. & Cooke, N. L. (1996). The effects of using manipulatives in teaching math problem solving to students with learning disabilities. *Learning Disabilities Research & Practice,* 11(1): 58–65.

Martino, A. M. & Maher, C. A. (1999). Teacher questioning to promote justification and generalization in mathematics: What research practice has taught us. *Journal of Mathematical Behavior,* 18(1): 53–78.

Moch, P. L. (Fall 2001). Manipulatives work! *The Educational Forum.*

Nunley, K. F. (1999). *Why hands-on tasks are good.* Salt Lake City, UT: Layered Curriculum.

Papert, S. (1980). *Mindstorms.* Scranton, PA: Basic Books.

Phillips, D. G. (1989) The development of logical thinking: A three-year longitudinal study. Paper presented to the National Council of Teachers of Mathematics, Orlando, FL.

Picciotto, H. (1998). Operation sense, tool-based pedagogy, curricular breadth: a proposal, accessed at http://www.picciotto.org.

Pugalee, D. K. (1999). Constructing a model of mathematical literacy. *The Clearing House* 73(1): 19–22.

Reisman, F. K. (1982). *A guide to the diagnostic teaching of arithmetic* (3rd ed.). Columbus, OH: Merrill.

Ross, R. & Kurtz, R. (1993). Making manipulatives work: A strategy for success. *The Arithmetic Teacher* (January 1993). 40: 254–258.

Ruzic, R. & O'Connell, K. (2001). Manipulatives. *Enhancement Literature Review,* accessed at http://www.cast.org/ncac/Manipulatives1666.cfm.

Sebesta, L. M. & Martin, S. R. M. (2004). Fractions: building a foundation with concrete manipulatives. *Illinois Schools Journal,* 83(2): 3–23.

Skemp, R. R. (1987). *The psychology of teaching mathematics* (revised American edition). Hillsdale, NJ: Erlbaum.

Smith, N. L., Babione, C., & Vick, B. J. (1999). Dumpling soup: Exploring kitchens, cultures, and mathematics. *Teaching Children Mathematics,* 6: 148–152.

Sowell, E. (1989). Effects of manipulative materials in mathematics instruction. *Journal for Research in Mathematics Education,* 20: 498–505.

Stein, M. K. & Bovalino, J. W. (2001). Manipulatives: One piece of the puzzle. *Mathematics Teaching in Middle School,* 6(6): 356–360.

Sugiyama, Y. (1987). Comparison of word problems in textbooks between Japan and the U.S. in J. P. Becker & T. Miwa (eds.), *Proceedings of U.S.–Japan Seminar on Problem Solving.* Carbondale, IL: Board of Trustees, Southern Illinois University.

Suydam, M. (1984). Research report: manipulative materials. *The Arithmetic Teacher,* 31: 27.

How to Use This Book

The goal of *Hands-On Standards* is to transition children from informal, concrete strategies to more formal, abstract ones. This book is based on the use of manipulatives, which are perfect tools for teaching and reinforcing learning. Manipulatives

- are meaningful to children;
- provide children with control and flexibility;
- mirror cognitive and mathematical structures in meaningful ways; and
- help children in connecting different types of knowledge.

Built around the manipulatives are activities that engage memory so that children more readily retain the mathematical concepts they learn.

The First Step

Before even opening the book, create a learning environment in which your children are excited about embarking on their mathematics adventure.

- First, take time to become familiar with the manipulatives and the lessons in which they are used.
- The lessons have been written to be used with common manipulatives. However, depending on the resources available, you may need to substitute one manipulative with another.
- Introduce your children to the manipulatives they will encounter. Have them investigate the manipulative kits in an unstructured way so that they will become familiar with all of the manipulative shapes and textures.
- Allow your children the time to discover the relationships between sizes and shapes. Let them have fun.
- Keep the manipulative kits in a special place. Make sure children know where the manipulatives are stored so that they can easily access them during math time and classroom free time.

Getting Ready

Once children have had time to use the manipulatives, walk them through a sample lesson.

- You might want to model an activity so children can see how you use the manipulatives.
- Make sure children know that there is a trial-and-error process they must go through so that they aren't self-conscious if they make errors.
- Tell children that you will all talk about the activities afterward and that they will be able to draw or write about the activities as well.

Using the Manual

The lessons in *Hands-On Standards* have been organized so that you can make an easy progression through the book. However, feel free to teach the lessons in any order to maximize children's learning. The following is a suggested plan for teaching each lesson:

- Read the story problem to the children. Ask them if they have ever had a similar problem. Let them tell you their experiences.

- Define any necessary vocabulary. Give children ways to use the words so they become familiar with the concepts.

- Divide the class into groups or pairs, depending on the directions. Show children the manipulatives they will be using. Give them a few minutes to get their supplies ready.

- While the lessons have been designed for use with individual children, pairs, or small groups, they can easily be adapted to meet your own classroom organization or teaching preference. Lessons can be used in centers or in a more traditional classroom setting.

- Lessons have been written for a fairly broad age range, for example, PreK–K. While the lessons serve as a guide, you should feel free to adapt data, vocabulary, and complexity to what you consider developmentally appropriate for your children.

- Help children perform the **Try It!** activity. Make sure they are having success as they work to understand the concept and develop an answer to the problem.

- Discuss the activity with children when they are finished. For suggestions, see the **Talk About It** section.

- Ask children to follow up the discussion by using the prompt in the **Solve It** section.

- Finally, have children work the problem in the **Standardized Practice** section without using manipulatives.

However you decide to use these lessons, make this manual your own. Use the ideas as jumping off points to enhance your teaching style and your existing math curriculum.

A Walk Through a Lesson

Each lesson in *Hands-On Standards* includes many features, including background information, objectives, pacing and grouping suggestions, discussion questions, and ideas for further activities, all in addition to the step-by-step, hands-on activity instruction. Take a walk through a lesson to see an explanation of each feature.

Objective
The **Objective** summarizes the skill or concept children will learn through the hands-on lesson.

Skills
The **Skills** box lists the top three mathematical skills that children will use in each lesson.

NCTM Expectations
Each lesson has been created to align with one or more of the grade-level expectations set by the National Council of Teachers of Mathematics (NCTM) in their *Principles and Standards for School Mathematics* (2000).

Talk About It
The **Talk About It** section provides post-activity discussion topics and questions. Discussion reinforces activity concepts and provides the opportunity to make sure children have learned and understood the concepts and skills.

Solve It
Solve It gives children a chance to show what they've learned. Children are asked to return to and solve the original word problem. They might summarize the lesson concept through drawing or writing, or extend the skill through a new variation on the problem.

Lesson Introduction
A brief introduction explores the background of the concepts and skills covered in each lesson. It shows how they fit into the larger context of children's mathematical development.

Try It! Arrow
In order to provide a transition from the introduction to the activity, an arrow draws attention to the Try It! activity on the next page. When the activity has been completed, return to the first page to complete the lesson.

LESSON **1**

Number and Operations

Counting to 5 and Back

Counting is the foundation for children's early work with numbers. Young children can associate number words with small collections of objects and gradually learn to count and keep track of objects in larger groups. They can establish one-to-one correspondence by moving, touching, or pointing to objects as they say number words. Children should learn that the next whole number in the counting sequence is one more than the previous number, and that the last number named represents the last object as well as the total number of objects.

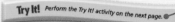

Try It! *Perform the Try It! activity on the next page.*

Objective

Count forward from 0 to 5 and backward from 5 to 0.

Skills

- Counting
- Using number words
- Recognizing numbers

NCTM Expectations

Number and Operations
- Count with understanding and recognize "how many" in sets of objects.
- Develop understanding of the relative position and magnitude of whole numbers and of ordinal and cardinal numbers and their connections.
- Connect number words and numerals to the quantities they represent, using various physical models and representations.

Talk About It
Discuss the Try It! activity.
- Have children talk about the process of counting from 0 to 5 and back.
- **Say:** *Let's count forward from 0 to 5.* **Ask:** *What number comes after 0? What number comes next?* Continue this line of questioning until all children have repeated the counting-forward sequence.
- **Say:** *Now let's count backward from 5 to 0.* **Ask:** *What number comes before 5? What number comes before 4?* Continue this line of questioning until all children have repeated the counting-backward sequence.

Solve It
With children, reread the problem. Invite them to draw a picture of the reading corner in James's classroom. Have them draw 5 reading mats and label them with the numbers 1–5, counting as they go.

More Ideas
For other ways to teach about counting to 5 and back—
- Have children draw circles (or trace around circle Attribute Blocks) on a sheet of paper and number the circles 1–5 to represent the buttons in an elevator. Partners can take turns pressing one of the "elevator buttons" and counting forward to that number to "ride" the elevator up, then counting backward to ride down.
- Have children use three to five 1" Color Cubes to create a simple building. Then have children count the number of cubes used forward and backward.

Standardized Practice
Have children try the following problem.

Count the cubes, starting with 1. How many cubes in all?

16

Talk About It
The **Talk About It** section provides post-activity discussion topics and questions. Discussion reinforces activity concepts and provides the opportunity to make sure children have learned and understood the concepts and skills.

More Ideas
More Ideas provides additional activities and suggestions for teaching about the lesson concept using a variety of manipulatives. These ideas might be suggestions for additional practice with the skill or an extension of the lesson.

Standardized Practice
Standardized Practice allows children to confront the lesson concept as they might encounter it on a standardized test.

Try It!

The **Try It!** activity opens with **Pacing** and **Grouping** guides. The **Pacing** guide indicates about how much time it will take for children to complete the activity, including the post-activity discussion. The **Grouping** guide recommends whether children should work independently, in pairs, or in small groups.

Next, the **Try It!** activity is introduced with a real-world story problem. Children will "solve" the problem by performing the hands-on activity. The word problem provides a context for the hands-on work and the lesson skill.

The **Materials** box lists the type and quantity of materials that children will use to complete the activity, including manipulatives such as Color Tiles and Pattern Blocks.

This section of the page also includes any instruction that children may benefit from before starting the activity, such as a review of foundational mathematical concepts or an introduction to new ones.

Try It! 15 minutes | Pairs
Here is a problem that involves counting to 5 and back.

Today is James's day to put down and pick up the mats in the reading corner. There are 5 children in James's reading group. James will count forward as he puts the mats in the reading corner and count backward as he picks up the mats. Can you help James count forward to 5 and back?

Introduce the problem. Then have children do the activity to solve the problem.

Give 5 Color Tiles to each pair of children. While displaying a tile, **say:** *Let's pretend that one of these tiles is a mat for the reading corner. The sheet of paper is the reading corner. We will place one tile on the sheet of paper for each child in James's reading group.*

Materials
- Color Tiles (5 per pair)
- paper (1 sheet per pair)

Number and Operations

1. To begin, ask children to make a circle shape with their hands. Tell children to say "zero" to show that there are no tiles on the paper.

2. Have children say "one" as they place a tile on the paper. Then have them place the other tiles on the paper one at a time as they count: two . . . three . . . four . . . five. When children get to 5, tell them to stand up, hold up their hands, and shout "Five!"

⚠ Look Out!

Emphasize that zero means "empty" or "none." But don't expect children to understand zero right away. Out of context, it is difficult for children to think of zero as a number, but as the initial or final part of a counting-up or counting-down sequence, the idea of zero as a number makes more sense to children.

3. Now have children take the tiles off the paper one at a time as they count backward: five . . . four . . . three . . . two . . . one . . . zero. When children get to 0, ask them to stand up, hold up their hands, and shout "Blastoff!"

17

A thumbnail image quickly identifies the main manipulative used in the Try It! activity.

Look Out!
Look Out! describes common errors or misconceptions likely to be exhibited by students at this age dealing with each skill or concept and offers troubleshooting suggestions.

Step-by-Step Activity Procedure
The hands-on activity itself is the core of each lesson. It is presented in three steps, each of which includes instruction in how children should use manipulatives and other materials to address the introductory word problem and master the lesson's skill or concept. An accompanying photograph illustrates each step.

NCTM Correlation Chart

*NCTM Standards/Expectations	Lessons
Number and Operations	
Understand numbers, ways of representing numbers, relationships among numbers, and number systems.	
Count with understanding and recognize "how many" in sets of objects.	NUM-1; NUM-2; NUM-3; NUM-4; NUM-5; NUM-6; NUM-7; NUM-8; NUM-9; NUM-10; NUM-11; DAT-1; DAT-2; DAT-3; DAT-4; DAT-5; DAT-6
Use multiple models to develop initial understandings of place value and the base-ten number system.	
Develop understanding of the relative postion and magnitude of whole numbers and of ordinal and cardinal numbers and their connections.	NUM-1; NUM-2; NUM-3; NUM-4; NUM-5; NUM-6; NUM-7; NUM-8; NUM-9; NUM-10; NUM-11; DAT-1; DAT-2; DAT-3; DAT-4; DAT-5; DAT-6
Develop a sense of whole numbers and represent and use them in flexible ways, including relating, composing, and decomposing numbers.	NUM-2; NUM-3; NUM-6; NUM-7; NUM-8; NUM-9; NUM-11; NUM-12; NUM-13; NUM-15
Connect number words and numerals to the quantities they represent, using various physical models and representations.	NUM-1; NUM-2; NUM-3; NUM-4; NUM-5; NUM-6; NUM-7; NUM-8; NUM-9
Understand and represent commonly used fractions, such as $\frac{1}{4}$, $\frac{1}{3}$, and $\frac{1}{2}$.	NUM-18
Understand meanings of operations and how they relate to one another.	
Understand various meanings of addition and subtraction of whole numbers and the relationship between the two operations.	NUM-14; NUM-15; NUM-16; NUM-17
Understand the effects of adding and subtracting whole numbers.	NUM-11; NUM-12; NUM-13; NUM-14; NUM-15; NUM-16; NUM-17
Understand situations that entail multiplication and division, such as equal groupings of objects and sharing equally.	NUM-18
Compute fluently and make reasonable estimates.	
Develop and use strategies for whole-number computations, with a focus on addition and subtraction.	NUM-11; NUM-12; NUM-13; NUM-16; NUM-17
Develop fluency with basic number combinations for addition and subtraction.	
Use a variety of methods and tools to compute, including objects, mental computation, estimation, paper and pencil, and calculators.	NUM-12; NUM-13; NUM-14; NUM-16; NUM-17

*NCTM Standards/Expectations	Lessons
Geometry	
Analyze characteristics and properties of two- and three-dimensional geometric shapes and develop mathematical arguments about geometric relationships.	
Recognize, name, build, draw, compare, and sort two- and three-dimensional shapes.	GEO-2; GEO-3; GEO-4; GEO-5; GEO-6; ALG-1; ALG-2; ALG-3
Describe attributes and parts of two- and three-dimensional shapes.	GEO-2; GEO-4; GEO-6; ALG-2
Investigate and predict the results of putting together and taking apart two- and three-dimensional shapes.	GEO-7
Specify locations and describe spatial relationships using coordinate geometry and other representational systems.	
Describe, name, and interpret relative positions in space and apply ideas about relative position.	GEO-1; GEO-9; GEO-10; GEO-11; GEO-12
Describe, name, and interpret direction and distance in navigating space and apply ideas about direction and distance.	
Find and name locations with simple relationships such as "near to" and in coordinate systems such as maps.	
Apply transformations and use symmetry to analyze mathematical situations.	
Recognize and apply slides, flips, and turns.	GEO-8
Recognize and create shapes that have symmetry.	
Use visualization, spatial reasoning, and geometric modeling to solve problems.	
Create mental images of geometric shapes using spatial memory and spatial visualization.	GEO-4; GEO-8
Recognize and represent shapes from different perspectives.	
Relate ideas in geometry to ideas in number and measurement.	
Recognize geometric shapes and structures in the environment and specify their location.	GEO-3

*NCTM Standards/Expectations	Lessons
Algebra	
Understand patterns, relations, and functions.	
Sort, classify, and order objects by size, number, and other properties.	ALG-1; ALG-2; ALG-3; ALG-4; ALG-5; ALG-6
Recognize, describe, and extend patterns such as sequences of sounds and shapes or simple numeric patterns and translate from one representation to another.	ALG-4; ALG-5; ALG-6; ALG-7; ALG-8
Analyze how both repeating and growing patterns are generated.	ALG-4; ALG-5; ALG-6; ALG-7; ALG-8
Represent and analyze mathematical situations and structures using algebraic symbols.	
Illustrate general principles and properties of operations, such as commutativity, using specific numbers.	
Use concrete, pictorial, and verbal representations to develop an understanding of invented and conventional symbolic notations.	
Use mathematical models to represent and understand quantitative relationships.	
Model situations that involve the addition and subtraction of whole numbers, using objects, pictures, and symbols.	NUM-14; ALG-9
Analyze change in various contexts.	
Describe qualitative change, such as a student's growing taller.	
Describe quantitative change, such as a student's growing two inches in one year.	

*NCTM Standards/Expectations	Lessons
Measurement	
Understand measurable attributes of objects and the units, systems, and processes of measurement.	
Recognize the attributes of length, volume, weight, area, and time.	MEA-1; MEA-2; MEA-3; MEA-6
Compare and order objects according to these attributes.	MEA-2; MEA-3
Understand how to measure using nonstandard and standard units.	MEA-1; MEA-3; MEA-4; MEA-6
Select an appropriate unit and tool for the attribute being measured.	
Apply appropriate techniques, tools, and formulas to determine measurements.	
Measure with multiple copies of units of the same size, such as paper clips laid end to end.	MEA-1; MEA-2; MEA-3; MEA-4; MEA-5; MEA-6
Use repetition of a single unit to measure something larger than the unit, for instance, measuring the length of a room with a single meterstick.	
Use tools to measure.	
Develop common referents for measures to make comparisons and estimates.	MEA-5

*NCTM Standards/Expectations	Lessons
Data Analysis and Probability	
Formulate questions that can be addressed with data and collect, organize, and display relevant data to answer them.	
Pose questions and gather data about themselves and their surroundings.	DAT-1; DAT-2; DAT-3; DAT-4
Sort and classify objects according to their attributes and organize data about the objects.	ALG-1; ALG-2; ALG-3; DAT-1; DAT-2; DAT-3; DAT-4
Represent data using concrete objects, pictures, and graphs.	DAT-1; DAT-2; DAT-3; DAT-4
Select and use appropriate statistical methods to analyze data.	
Describe parts of the data and the set of data as a whole to determine what the data show.	DAT-1; DAT-2; DAT-4
Develop and evaluate inferences and predictions that are based on data.	
Discuss events in students' experiences as likely or unlikely.	DAT-5; DAT-6

Number and Operations

Number pervades all areas of mathematics and is, therefore, a cornerstone of elementary mathematics education. **Operations**—the use of numbers to add, subtract, multiply, and divide—give children the tools to solve real-life problems. Together, **Number** and **Operations** combine to form the core of elementary mathematics instruction to give children greater number sense and more fluency in performing arithmetic operations.

In the primary grades, one main area of focus is on developing number sense. Children at this level are expected to quantify objects and understand how numbers relate to one another. With a rich understanding of numbers and our base-ten number system, children can manipulate and think of numbers in a variety of ways.

Another main area of focus is on building computational fluency. To ensure future mathematical success, children must develop efficient and accurate methods for adding and subtracting, be able to explain their methods, understand that there are a variety of ways to solve a problem, and be able to estimate and judge whether an answer is reasonable.

Manipulatives help children develop both number sense and computational fluency. Children will gain a deeper understanding of math concepts than they would by simply memorizing algorithms.

The Grades Pre-K–2 NCTM Standards for Number and Operations suggest that children should:

- Understand numbers, ways of representing numbers, relationships among numbers, and number systems
- Understand meanings of operations and how they relate to one another
- Compute fluently and make reasonable estimates

As primary-grade children develop an understanding of number and operations, they are building a foundation upon which future mathematical concepts can be built. During these formative years, teachers help children move from basic counting techniques to more sophisticated mathematical concepts, such as relationships among numbers, patterns, estimation, and place value. The following are activities involving manipulatives that children can use to develop skills in **Number and Operations.**

Number and Operations

Contents

Number and Operations

Counting to 5 and Back

Counting is the foundation for children's early work with numbers. Young
children can associate number words with small collections of objects and
gradually learn to count and keep track of objects in larger groups. They can
establish one-to-one correspondence by moving, touching, or pointing to
objects as they say number words. Children should learn that the next whole
number in the counting sequence is one more than the previous number, and
that the last number named represents the last object as well as the total
number of objects.

Try It! *Perform the Try It! activity on the next page.*

Talk About It

Discuss the Try It! activity.

- Have children talk about the process of counting from 0 to 5 and back.
- Say: *Let's count forward from 0 to 5.* Ask: *What number comes after 0?
  What number comes next?* Continue this line of questioning until all
  children have repeated the counting-forward sequence.
- Say: *Now let's count backward from 5 to 0.* Ask: *What number comes
  before 5? What number comes before 4?* Continue this line of questioning
  until all children have repeated the counting-backward sequence.

Solve It

With children, reread the problem. Invite them to draw a picture of the
reading corner in James's classroom. Have them draw 5 reading mats and label
them with the numbers 1–5, counting as they go.

More Ideas

For other ways to teach about counting to 5 and back—

- Have children draw circles (or trace around circle Attribute Blocks) on a
  sheet of paper and number the circles 1–5 to represent the buttons in an
  elevator. Partners can take turns pressing one of the "elevator buttons" and
  counting forward to that number to "ride" the elevator up, then counting
  backward to ride down.
- Have children use three to five 1" Color Cubes to create a simple building.
  Then have children count the number of cubes used forward and backward.

Standardized Practice

Have children try the following problem.

Count the cubes, starting with 1. How many cubes in all?

Try It! 15 minutes | Pairs

Here is a problem that involves counting to 5 and back.

Today is James's day to put down and pick up the mats in the reading corner. There are 5 children in James's reading group. James will count forward as he puts the mats in the reading corner and count backward as he picks up the mats. Can you help James count forward to 5 and back?

Introduce the problem. Then have children do the activity to solve the problem.

Give 5 Color Tiles to each pair of children. While displaying a tile, **say:** *Let's pretend that one of these tiles is a mat for the reading corner. The sheet of paper is the reading corner. We will place one tile on the sheet of paper for each child in James's reading group.*

Materials
- Color Tiles (5 per pair)
- paper (1 sheet per pair)

1. To begin, ask children to make a circle shape with their hands. Tell children to say "zero" to show that there are no tiles on the paper.

2. Have children say "one" as they place a tile on the paper. Then have them place the other tiles on the paper one at a time as they count: two . . . three . . . four . . . five. When children get to 5, tell them to stand up, hold up their hands, and shout "Five!"

⚠ Look Out!

Emphasize that zero means "empty" or "none." But don't expect children to understand zero right away. Out of context, it is difficult for children to think of zero as a number, but as the initial or final part of a counting-up or counting-down sequence, the idea of zero as a number makes more sense to children.

3. Now have children take the tiles off the paper one at a time as they count backward: five . . . four . . . three . . . two . . . one . . . zero. When children get to 0, ask them to stand up, hold up their hands, and shout "Blastoff!"

2

Number and Operations

Groups of 0 to 5

Representing numbers with various physical materials and relating them to number words and numerals is a major part of mathematics instruction in the early elementary grades. As children gain understanding of numbers and how to represent them, they build a foundation for understanding relationships among numbers.

Objective

Identify a number for a group of 0 to 5 objects.

Skills

• Counting
• Reading and writing numbers
• Representing numbers

NCTM Expectations

Number and Operations
• Count with understanding and recognize "how many" in sets of objects.
• Develop understanding of the relative position and magnitude of whole numbers and of ordinal and cardinal numbers and their connections.
• Develop a sense of whole numbers and represent and use them in flexible ways, including relating, composing, and decomposing numbers.
• Connect number words and numerals to the quantities they represent, using various physical models and representations.

Try It! *Perform the Try It! activity on the next page.*

Talk About It

Discuss the Try It! activity.

■ Hold up Number Card 3 (BLM 1). **Ask:** *What number is this?* **Say:** *Show me 3 fingers.* **Ask:** *How do you know how many fingers to hold up?* Repeat for the other numbers.

■ **Ask:** *What does a group of zero look like?* **Say:** *Show me with your hands.*

Solve It

With children, reread the problem. Then have children pretend that they are going on a field trip. Ask them to arrange themselves in groups of 5. Have them draw a picture showing all the children in their group and label it using numerals.

More Ideas

For other ways to teach about identifying and representing numbers—

■ Give children instructions for making groups using specific numbers and colors of Snap Cubes®; for example, **say:** *Make a group of 4 blue Cubes. Make a group of red Cubes that is the same as the group of blue Cubes. Make a group of 0 green Cubes.*

■ For children needing extra help with 0, have them count out 5 counters into a paper cup, then count backward to 0 as they remove each counter from the cup. Guide children to understand that now that there are 0 counters in the cup, the cup is empty.

Standardized Practice

Have children try the following problem.

Draw dots to match each number card. The first one has been done for you.

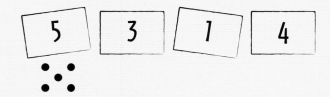

Try It! 30 minutes | Pairs

Here is a problem that relates to groups of 0 to 5.

The children are going to see a musical at another school. Before boarding the bus for their trip, their teacher holds up a card with the number 5 and says, "Yesterday we learned about the number 5. Before we go, I need everyone to line up in groups of 5." How will the children know what to do?

Introduce the problem. Then have children do the activity to solve the problem.

Give Snap Cubes®, crayons, Number Cards 0–5 (BLM 1), and 5 blank index cards to each pair of children.

Materials
- Snap Cubes® (13 per pair)
- Number Cards (BLM 1; 1 set of 0–5 per pair)
- index cards (15 per pair)
- crayons (1 per child)

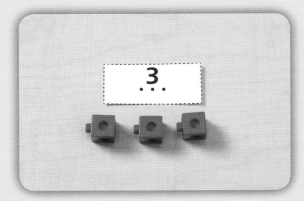

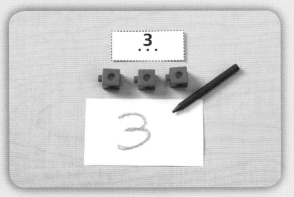

1. Help children place the Number Cards facedown on the table. To begin, have a child from each group pick a card and make a group of Cubes to represent that number.

2. Now ask the other children to check their partner's work by counting the Cubes again. Have them write the corresponding numeral on a blank index card.

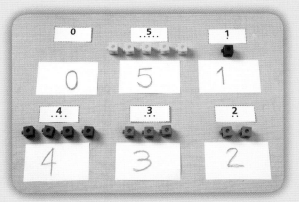

3. Have children switch roles. Encourage children to continue working until all Number Cards have been used.

⚠ Look Out!

Watch for children who cannot create a group for a specific number. Have them count forward from 1 as they touch each Cube. Also, watch for children who count the same Cube twice. Have them line up the Cubes in one row and count them from left to right.

Objective

Identify a number for a group of 6 to 10 objects.

Skills

- Counting
- Representing numbers
- Writing numbers

NCTM Expectations

Number and Operations
- Count with understanding and recognize "how many" in sets of objects.
- Develop understanding of the relative position and magnitude of whole numbers and of ordinal and cardinal numbers and their connections.
- Develop a sense of whole numbers and represent and use them in flexible ways, including relating, composing, and decomposing numbers.
- Connect number words and numerals to the quantities they represent, using various physical models and representations.

Number and Operations

Groups of 6 to 10

A key to mathematical understanding for young children is making the link between the concrete and the abstract—between physical models and written symbols. In this activity, children will represent numbers 6 to 10 by grouping objects and identifying the corresponding numerals.

Try It! *Perform the Try It! activity on the next page.*

Talk About It

Discuss the Try It! activity.

- Have groups talk about their Bug Zoos. Hold up a Number Card (BLM 1). **Ask:** *How many Backyard Bugs™ would you put in this cage?* **Say:** *Say the number. Now show me with your fingers.* Repeat for all numbers.

- Stress the words *most* and *fewest.* **Say:** *Point to the cage with the most Bugs.* **Ask:** *How do you know it has the most Bugs?* **Say:** *Point to the cage with the fewest Bugs.* **Ask:** *How do you know it has the fewest Bugs?*

- Point to a cage and hold up the Number Card. **Ask:** *What if I took one Bug out of this cage? How many Bugs would be left? How many would there be if I put one more in this cage?*

Solve It

With children, reread the problem. Then have children draw a picture showing 5 Bug Zoos, labeled 6 to 10. Have them draw the appropriate number of Bugs in each zoo.

More Ideas

For other ways to teach about identifying and representing numbers—

- Display a Number Card and have children count out a group of Snap Cubes®, Link 'N' Learn® Links, Three Bear Family® Counters, or other small items to match the number.

- Write the numbers 6, 7, 8, 9, and 10 in order on the chalkboard. Have children build Snap Cube towers to match the numbers. Then have them push their towers together to recreate a city skyline! Point out how the towers in the skyline get taller from left to right.

Standardized Practice

Have children try the following problem.

Count the stars. Write that number.

☆ ☆ ☆ ☆ ☆ ☆ ☆ ☆

Try It! 30 minutes | Groups of 5

Here is a problem about identifying, reading, and representing numbers.

Tara's class is putting Backyard Bugs™ in cages to make a Bug Zoo. Each cage has a number on it to tell how many Bugs to put in the cage. How will Tara know if she put the correct number of Bugs in each cage?

Introduce the problem. Then have children do the activity to solve the problem.

Give Bugs, paper, crayons, and Number Cards 6–10 (BLM 1) to each group of children.

Materials
- Backyard Bugs™ (40 per group)
- Number Cards (BLM 1; 1 set of 6–10 per group)
- half-sheets of paper (5 per group)
- crayons (at least 4 per group)

1. Invite members of the group to create a "Bug Zoo" that has 5 "cages" (half-sheets of paper), each containing from 6 to 10 Bugs. (One cage should have 6 Bugs, one cage should have 7 Bugs, and so on.)

2. Have group members count the Bugs in each cage to verify that they contain only 6, 7, 8, 9, or 10 Bugs.

3. Have children find the Number Card that matches each cage.

⚠ Look Out!

Watch for children who cannot create a group for a specific number. Have them count forward from 1 as they touch each item.

LESSON

4

Number and Operations

Number Shapes

In this lesson, children develop their "number sense" by investigating numbers in different arrangements. This kind of work provides children with an opportunity to practice their counting skills, helps children develop some visual sense about quantity as they see same-number groups arranged in different ways, and helps children to expand their number sense as they begin to realize that a group of 7, for example, is always 7 no matter how the group is arranged.

Try It! *Perform the Try It! activity on the next page.*

Talk About It

Discuss the Try It! activity.

- Have children refer to one of the Number Shapes Worksheet (BLM 2) exercises.
- **Ask:** *What does Bryan's shape look like to you? How many Snap Cubes® is it made of? How do you know?* (Repeat for Tina's shape.)
- **Ask:** *How are the shapes alike? How are they different?*
- Guide children to understand that a number can be arranged in many different ways and still be the same number.

Solve It

With children, reread the problem. Then have children rebuild the shapes described in the problem with Cubes and explain if Bryan's logic was correct. For enrichment, have children find several shapes for the number 5.

More Ideas

For other ways to teach about number arrangements—

- Have children build number shapes with Pattern Blocks. First, assign each child a number from 4 to 6. Then ask children to build 6 different shapes with their number of blocks. Each shape should be made with a different block shape.
- Assign pairs of children a number from 4 to 10. Give each pair a corresponding number of 1" Color Cubes. Challenge children to build as many different cube shapes as possible for their number.

Standardized Practice

Have children try the following problem.

Which two shapes have 6 Cubes? Circle them.

  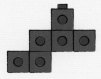

Objective

Explore different arrangements of the same number.

Skills

- Counting
- Representing numbers
- Visual thinking

NCTM Expectations

Number and Operations
- Count with understanding and recognize "how many" in sets of objects.
- Develop understanding of the relative position and magnitude of whole numbers and of ordinal and cardinal numbers and their connections.
- Connect number words and numerals to the quantities they represent, using various physical models and representations.

Try It! 30 minutes | Independent

Here is a problem about number arrangements.

Mrs. Kim gave each child some Snap Cubes® to build with. Bryan connected his Cubes in a line to build a long stick shape. Tina connected her Cubes in the shape of the letter T. Bryan says that his shape has more Cubes because it is longer than Tina's shape. Is Bryan correct?

Introduce the problem. Then have children do the activity to solve the problem.

Give 24 Cubes and a Number Shapes Worksheet (BLM 2) to each child.

Materials
- Snap Cubes® (24 per child)
- Number Shapes Worksheet (BLM 2; 1 per child)

1. Have children build Bryan's shape in Exercise 1 on the worksheet. Ask them to count the Cubes and write the number.

2. Now have children build Tina's shape in Exercise 1 on the worksheet. Ask them to count the Cubes and write the number. **Ask:** *Do the shapes have the same number of Cubes? How can you tell?*

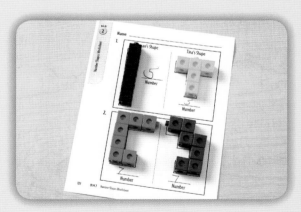

3. Have children tell how the shapes are the same and how they are different. Then have children repeat for worksheet Exercise 2.

⚠ Look Out!

Watch for children who have difficulty understanding that the same number can "look" many different ways. Give these children 10 Cubes. Have them arrange 5 Cubes in 2 different ways. Then have children compare the shapes side-by-side and count the number of Cubes in each shape.

5

Objective

Estimate and count groups of objects to 10.

Skills

- Counting
- Estimating
- Representing numbers

NCTM Expectations

Number and Operations

- Count with understanding and recognize "how many" in sets of objects.
- Develop understanding of the relative position and magnitude of whole numbers and of ordinal and cardinal numbers and their connections.
- Connect number words and numerals to the quantities they represent, using various physical models and representations.

Number and Operations

Estimate and Count

Young children must have varied opportunities to continue to develop, use, and practice counting groups of objects. Children often use different strategies for dealing with smaller versus larger groups. For example, some children may look at a small group of objects and recognize "how many," but they may need to physically count larger sets to find the total number of objects. The ability to recognize small groups within a larger group supports the development of visually grouping objects as a strategy for estimating quantities.

Try It! Perform the Try It! activity on the next page.

Talk About It

Discuss the Try It! activity.

- Have children talk about how they made their estimates. **Ask:** *How can you tell when there are a lot of Link 'N' Learn® Links in the bag? How can you tell when there are only a few Links in the bag?*

- Pass a bag containing 5 Links around to the children. Let them feel the bag, shake it, and listen for sounds. **Ask:** *Do you think this bag has more than 5 Links, less than 5 Links, or about 5 Links? What is your estimate?*

- **Ask:** *Which numbers do you think would be easy to estimate? Which numbers would be harder to estimate? Why do you think so?*

Solve It

With children, reread the problem. Have children talk about the things they would do to estimate the number of Links in the bag if they were John.

More Ideas

For other ways to teach about estimating and counting—

- Have children make bracelets using Link 'N' Learn Links. Before children start, have them get a feel for the size of 1 Link. Then have them estimate how many Links they think they will need to make a bracelet. Finally, have children build the bracelets and count the Links. How close were their estimates?

- Have children make "estimation cups" by filling paper cups with up to 5 small objects, such as Snap Cubes® or Link 'N' Learn Links. Children can trade cups with other classmates and try to estimate the number of objects.

Standardized Practice

Have children try the following problem.

How many stars do you see in the circle?
Make an estimate and then count.
How close was your estimate?

Try It! 15 minutes | Pairs

Here is a problem about estimating and counting.

John's school is having a carnival. One stall has an estimating game. Children play by estimating how many Link 'N' Learn® Links are in a paper bag without looking in the bag. How can John estimate how many Links are in the bag?

Introduce the problem. Then have children do the activity to solve the problem.

Discuss the term *estimate* with children. Then give each pair a paper bag and 10 Links. Pick one child in each pair to be the "Counter." The other child will be the "Estimator."

Materials
- Link 'N' Learn® Links (10 per pair)
- paper bags (1 per pair)

1. Invite the "Counters" to count out a number of Links and place them in a bag. Tell these children that the number of Links in the bag is a secret and they should not tell the "Estimators."

2. Ask the "Estimators" to estimate how many Links are in the bag. (Have some Links available for these children to use as reference.) Tell them that they can feel the bag and shake it, but not open it. **Ask:** *Can you tell how many are in the bag by quickly feeling, shaking, and listening?* **Say:** *When you think you know the number, say the number out loud.*

3. Have children talk about the reasons for their guesses. **Ask:** *Why did you guess that number?* Then ask the "Estimators" to empty the bag of Links onto the table and count them. How close were children's estimates? Have children switch roles and repeat the activity with a different number of Links.

⚠ Look Out!

Watch for children who make unreasonable estimates. Remind these children to use the loose Links as reference for their estimates.

Number and Operations

Comparing Groups

This lesson extends children's investigations of numbers to 10 and takes on the additional focus of comparison. Children will count but will also be engaged in comparing two groups. Children will find that there are lots of ways to talk about how two groups compare.

Objective

Compare groups of 1 to 10 objects.

Skills

- Counting
- Comparing
- Recognizing numbers

NCTM Expectations

Number and Operations

- Count with understanding and recognize "how many" in sets of objects.
- Develop understanding of the relative position and magnitude of whole numbers and of ordinal and cardinal numbers and their connections.
- Develop a sense of whole numbers and represent and use them in flexible ways, including relating, composing, and decomposing numbers.
- Connect number words and numerals to the quantities they represent, using various physical models and representations.

Try It! *Perform the Try It! activity on the next page.*

Talk About It

Discuss the Try It! activity.

- Have two volunteers come to the front of the class to demonstrate the game they played during the Try It! activity.
- After the pair picks their cards, have them display the card showing the number of blankets and the card showing the number of Three Bear Family® Counters to the class. **Say:** *Make a guess.* **Ask:** *Do you think the number of blankets is less than the number of Bears? More than the number of Bears? The same as the number of Bears? Why did you make that guess?*
- Then have volunteers set up the actual number of blankets and seat the Bears. **Ask:** *Is the number of blankets less than the number of Bears? More than the number of Bears? The same as the number of Bears? Was your guess correct?*

Solve It

With children, reread the problem. Tell children that they are the Bears and that they will be using sheets of construction paper for blankets. Invite two volunteers to be in charge of picking the cards. Encourage children to make a guess about the number of blankets and the number of Bears. Select the number of volunteers required by the "Bears" card. Have children set up the correct number of blankets and seat themselves to check their guesses.

More Ideas

For other ways to teach about comparing groups—

- Have children use Link 'N' Learn® Links to create two chains of different sizes. Have them compare the two chains using the terms *more than* or *less than*.
- Have each child in a pair pull a handful of Snap Cubes® from a paper bag filled with Cubes. Then have children count the Cubes, compare the groups, and describe the groups using the terms *less than, more than,* or *same number.*

Standardized Practice

Have children try the following problem.

Is the number of squares less than, more than, or the same as the number of Bears?

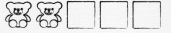

Try It! 30 minutes | Pairs

Here is a problem about counting and comparing groups.

Tara's class is playing a game. They pick a number to show how many blankets and a number to show how many Three Bear Family® Counters. Then they seat the Bears on the blankets. Sometimes there will be enough blankets, and sometimes there won't. Do you think the number of blankets is less than the number of Bears? Do you think the number of blankets is more than the number of Bears? Do you think the number of blankets is the same as the number of Bears?

Introduce the problem. Then have children do the activity to solve the problem. Tell children to pretend that the Color Tiles are blankets. Distribute Bear Counters, 10 tiles, and Number Cards 1–10 (BLM 1) to each pair.

Materials
- Three Bear Family® Counters (10 per pair)
- Color Tiles (10 per pair)
- Number Cards (BLM 1; 2 sets of 1–10 cards per pair)

1. Instruct children to mix up the cards and place them facedown in a stack. Have partners decide who will set up the blankets (tiles) and who will seat the Bears on the blankets. Ask each child to draw a card (one for blankets and one for Bears).

2. Have children identify the number of blankets and Bears and make a guess about whether the number of blankets is less than, more than, or the same as the number of Bears. Then have children count out the number of blankets and Bears to show each group.

3. Instruct partners to set up the blankets and seat the Bears. Ask children to compare the groups and decide whether the number of blankets is less than, more than, or the same as the number of Bears.

⚠ Look Out!

Some children may be more focused on seating Bears and making sure that all Bears have a blanket instead of comparing groups. Have these children line up the Bears in front of the blankets to show the one-to-one correspondence. This way, children will more easily identify whether the number of blankets is less than, more than, or the same as the number of Bears.

27

Number and Operations

Equal Groups

Having had a certain amount of rote-counting practice, children should be ready to develop an understanding of the relative magnitude of whole numbers. They practice this skill by matching and comparing groups of objects using one-to-one correspondence.

Try It! *Perform the Try It! activity on the next page.*

Talk About It

Discuss the Try It! activity.

- **Say:** *Remember, we use the math word* equal *to describe two groups that have the same number.*

- **Ask:** *How can you tell when two chains have the same, or an equal, number of Link 'N' Learn® Links?*

- **Say:** *Here are two chains that have different numbers of Links.* (Display two chains, one made of 3 Links and the other made of 4 Links.) **Ask:** *What could you do to make these two the same, or equal?*

Solve It

With children, reread the problem. Have children draw a picture showing the players on the two kickball teams. Have children draw lines to match the children in the picture, using one-to-one correspondence.

More Ideas

For other ways to teach about equal groups—

- Have children draw a straight line across a sheet of paper to create two workspaces. Have them make a line of 5 Snap Cubes® in each workspace. Ask children to draw lines to match the Cubes in each group one-to-one.

- Have children arrange three 1" Color Cubes of one color in a line, then place three cubes of another color on top of the first ones. Have children confirm that the second group has the same number of cubes as the first.

Standardized Practice

Have children try the following problem.

Draw a chain that has an equal number of Links as this one.

Objective

Match objects using one-to-one correspondence to demonstrate equal groups.

Skills

- Counting
- Grouping
- Matching one-to-one

NCTM Expectations

Number and Operations
- Count with understanding and recognize "how many" in sets of objects.
- Develop understanding of the relative position and magnitude of whole numbers and of ordinal and cardinal numbers and their connections.
- Develop a sense of whole numbers and represent and use them in flexible ways, including relating, composing, and decomposing numbers.
- Connect number words and numerals to the quantities they represent, using various physical models and representations.

Try It! 15 minutes | Pairs

Here is a problem about equal groups.

Children in Mr. Smith's class are playing kickball at recess. Josh, Tara, Stacey, Juan, and Brian are on Team 1. Phil, Marcia, Ivette, Billy, and Ling are on Team 2. Do the teams have an equal number of children?

Introduce the problem. Then have children do the activity to solve the problem.

Discuss the term *equal.* Tell children that two groups that have the same number of objects are *equal.* Point out specific examples of equal groups of objects or people. Distribute Link 'N' Learn® Links to each pair.

Materials
• Link 'N' Learn® Links (10 per pair in 2 colors)

1. Ask children to pretend that the Links are children on the kickball teams. Have one child in each pair make a chain of up to 5 Links, using one color of Link.

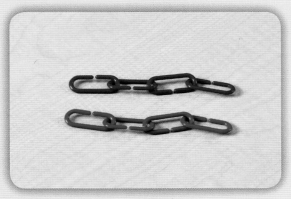

2. Now ask the other child in each pair to make an equal chain using a different color. Have partners check each other's chains to verify that the chains have an equal number of Links.

3. Extend the activity by having each partner independently make a new chain with up to 5 Links. Have partners compare their chains and count the Links to reinforce the concepts of *more, fewer,* and *equal.*

⚠ Look Out!

Watch for children who cannot determine whether the chains have an equal number of Links. Have these children align the chains and match the Links one-to-one.

Objective

Identify and create groups that have one more object than another group.

Skills

- Counting
- Comparing
- Representing numbers

NCTM Expectations

Number and Operations
- Count with understanding and recognize "how many" in sets of objects.
- Develop understanding of the relative position and magnitude of whole numbers and of ordinal and cardinal numbers and their connections.
- Develop a sense of whole numbers and represent and use them in flexible ways, including relating, composing, and decomposing numbers.
- Connect number words and numerals to the quantities they represent, using various physical models and representations.

Number and Operations

More and Fewer

Relative value is an important concept of number sense. By learning the concepts *more* and *fewer,* children begin to use the language of mathematics to compare quantities. This understanding lays the foundation for beginning addition and subtraction skills.

Try It! *Perform the Try It! activity on the next page.*

Talk About It

Discuss the Try It! activity.

- **Say:** *I have two equal Snap Cube® trains.* (Display two equal Cube trains, one red and one yellow. Remind children that when two groups have the same number, they are equal.) *I'm going to connect another Cube to the red train.* **Ask:** *Are the trains equal now? How do you know?*

- **Say:** *Tell me about the red train.* **Ask:** *Does it have more Cubes, fewer Cubes, or the same number of Cubes as the yellow train?* **Say:** *Show me how you can tell.*

- **Say:** *Now tell me about the yellow train.* **Ask:** *Does it have more Cubes, fewer Cubes, or the same number of Cubes as the red train? How do you know?*

Solve It

With children, reread the problem. Have children draw a picture showing Maria's building blocks and Jordan's building blocks. Have them write the number of blocks next to each group. Ask children to explain their drawings, using the terms *more* and *fewer.*

More Ideas

For other ways to teach about *more* and *fewer*—

- Have each child in a pair pull a handful of Snap Cubes from a bag. Children can count the Cubes and compare the groups to establish *more, fewer,* or *equal.*

- Let small groups of children build three long chains of Link 'N' Learn® Links. When groups are finished, they can compare the chains. Which chains are equal? Which chain has more Links than the other two chains? Which chain has fewer Links than the other two chains?

Standardized Practice

Have children try the following problem.

Draw a new train that has 1 more Cube. Tell how you know the new train has 1 more.

Try It! 15 minutes | Pairs

Here is a problem about *more* and *fewer*.

The children in Mr. Byrd's class are having fun making buildings with the new building blocks. Each one wants to have more of the new blocks than anyone else. Maria says she has 4 new blocks. Jordan says he has one more block than Maria. How can Maria find out the number of blocks Jordan has?

Introduce the problem. Then have children do the activity to solve the problem.

Give 5 Snap Cubes® of one color and 5 Cubes of another color to each pair of children.

Materials
• Snap Cubes® (10 per pair)

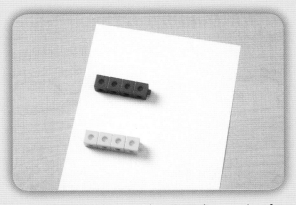

1. Have one child in each pair make a train of 4 Cubes. Ask their partners to make an equal train using a different color. Have children line up the second train below the first.

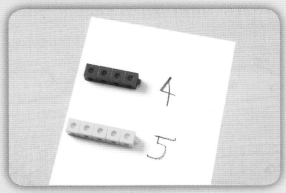

2. Tell children to add a Cube to the bottom train. Then have children count the Cubes in each train and write the numbers. **Ask:** *Are the trains the same or different? Which train has 1 more Cube than the other? How do you know? Which train has 1 fewer Cube? How do you know?*

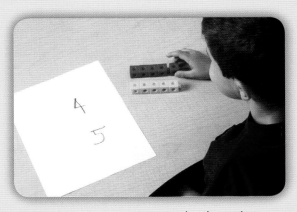

3. Say: *Now I want you to make the trains equal. Show me how to do this.* Children should add one Cube to the top train so both trains have an equal number of Cubes.

⚠ Look Out!

Some children may confuse the terms *more, fewer,* and *equal*. Reinforce these terms throughout the day by pointing out that *more* children are in their chairs than are sitting on the floor, that there are *fewer* red Cubes in the trains than yellow Cubes, and that each child in the class gets an *equal* amount of food for a snack. Remind children that *equal* means *same*.

Number and Operations

Order of Numbers

Although many young children are able to count, often they have not yet developed an understanding of what the numbers mean. It is important that children develop a one-to-one correspondence between numbers and sets of objects. By learning and practicing this concept, children also learn the concept of sequencing, or order.

Try It! *Perform the Try It! activity on the next page.*

Talk About It

Discuss the Try It! activity.

- **Say:** *Let's count to 5.* **Ask:** *What number do we say first when we count?* **Say:** *Make a chain that shows 1.* **Ask:** *What number comes after 1?* **Say:** *Now make a chain that shows 2.* **Ask:** *How do you know that 2 comes after 1?*

- Repeat this line of questioning for other numbers. Elicit from children that, when counting forward by ones, each number is one more than the number before it.

Solve It

With children, reread the problem. Then take the class out to the playground. Divide children into pairs, and give each pair some chalk and Link 'N' Learn® Links. Help pairs draw hopscotch patterns. Have children solve the problem by numbering the boxes in order from 1 to 5. Then let children play hopscotch using the Links as markers.

More Ideas

For other ways to teach about the order of numbers 1 through 5—

- Have children use Snap Cubes® to make one train for each number from 1 to 5. Have them use one color for each train. Then have them line up the trains in order from 1 to 5.

- Provide one set of Number Cards 1–5 (BLM 1) and counters at a center. Instruct children to make sets of objects to match each number. Children can place counters on the dots for self-checking and reinforcement. Extend the activity by providing a reverse order of numbers (5, 4, 3, 2, 1) and a mixed order of numbers (for example, 2, 1, 3, 5, 4).

Standardized Practice

Have children try the following problem.

Which set of dots is in order from 1 to 3? Circle it.

A. ● ●● ●●●   B. ●● ●●● ●

Objective

Explore the order of numbers 1 to 5.

Skills

- Counting
- Representing numbers
- Sequencing

NCTM Expectations

Number and Operations
- Count with understanding and recognize "how many" in sets of objects.
- Develop understanding of the relative position and magnitude of whole numbers and of ordinal and cardinal numbers and their connections.
- Develop a sense of whole numbers and represent and use them in flexible ways, including relating, composing, and decomposing numbers.
- Connect number words and numerals to the quantities they represent, using various physical models and representations.

Try It! **15 minutes | Pairs**

Here is a problem about number order.

At recess, Jenna's teacher drew a hopscotch pattern on the sidewalk. She asked Jenna to number the boxes from 1 to 5. This is how Jenna numbered the boxes. Jenna's teacher asked her why she ordered the numbers this way. Jenna said that 2 is one more than 3, so it comes after. Is Jenna correct?

5
4
2
3
1

Introduce the problem. Then have children do the activity to solve the problem.

Give a set of index cards and 15 assorted Link 'N' Learn® Links to each child. Children will need enough of an assortment so that they can build chains using five different colors.

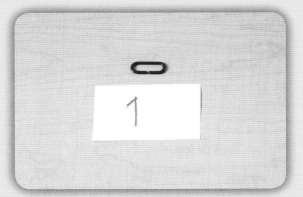

1. Have children make and place a card with the number 1 in front of them. Ask children to build a chain made of one Link and place it above the card.

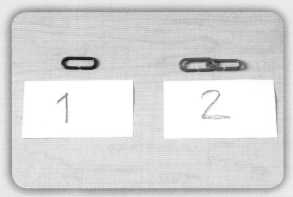

2. Now have children build a different-color chain that has one more Link than the first chain. Have them place this second chain near the first chain for comparison. Ask children to make a number card that matches and place it below the new chain.

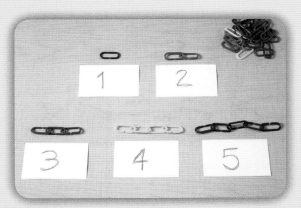

3. Using different colors for each chain, have children make cards and build chains for the numbers 3–5. Then guide children to order the numbers and chains like the vertical hopscotch pattern.

⚠ Look Out!

Children may have difficulty matching the numbers to the corresponding sets. Encourage children to count the items in the set, touching each item as it is counted. Remind them that the last number they say when counting names that set. For children still struggling, provide "landing spots," such as small circles, in which children can place Links before connecting them below Number Cards.

Objective

Identify ordinal numbers from first through fifth.

Skills

- Counting
- Numeration
- Sequencing

NCTM Expectations

Number and Operations
- Count with understanding and recognize "how many" in sets of objects.
- Develop understanding of the relative position and magnitude of whole numbers and of ordinal and cardinal numbers and their connections.

Number and Operations

Ordinal Numbers

Children are faced with real-life situations involving ordinal numbers every day when they are standing in line or listening to the sequence of events in a story. While many children are able to count from one to five, this does not mean that they understand ordinal numbers. Some cardinal and ordinal numbers correlate more easily to one another than do others. Children need instruction and practice to master ordinal numbers.

Try It! *Perform the Try It! activity on the next page.*

Talk About It

Discuss the Try It! activity.

- **Ask:** *What word describes the place that comes after first? What comes before third? What comes after fourth?* (Ask children a series of questions emphasizing the words *next, before,* and *after.* Encourage children to use ordinal number words as they reply to these questions.)

- **Say:** *I have a chain with five Link 'N' Learn® Links.* (Display a chain of five Links for the class.) *As I point to each Link in the chain, say which place it is in.* (Start with the first Link and go through the fifth, and then go back to the first.)

Solve It

With children, reread the problem. Then give each child five sheets of paper. Instruct children to draw pictures to show Andre, Tammi, Kara, Marco, and Lila. Then have children use the pictures to show each child's place in line. **Ask:** *How do you know Kara's place in line?*

More Ideas

For other ways to teach about ordinal numbers—

- Give each child five different-colored 1" Color Cubes. Explain that to make a "fruit salad," they should add a purple cube first, a yellow cube second, an orange cube third, a green cube fourth, and a red cube fifth. Then have children arrange the "fruit" in the correct order.

- Give each pair of children five different Backyard Bugs™. Tell children that they are going to line up the Bugs to march in a bug parade. Have them follow your directions as they order the Bugs. For example, the spider is first, the fly is second, the grasshopper is third, and so on through fifth.

Standardized Practice

Have children try the following problem.

Color the first bear red. Color the second bear blue. Color the third bear green.

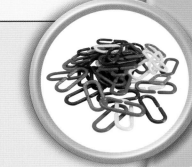

Try It! 15 minutes | Pairs

Here is a problem demonstrating ordinal numbers.

Kara is in line at the school library to check out a book. Andre is first, Tammi is second, Kara is after Tammi, Marco is fourth, and Lila is fifth. What is Kara's place in line?

Introduce the problem. Invite five volunteers to stand in line at the front of the room. Then ask the class to repeat after you as you point to each volunteer and say the cardinal number followed by the corresponding ordinal number (one, first; two, second; three, third; four, fourth; five, fifth). Then have children do the activity to solve the problem. Distribute 5 Link 'N' Learn® Links to each child.

Materials
- Link 'N' Learn® Links (1 red, 1 orange, 1 yellow, 1 green, and 1 blue Link per child)

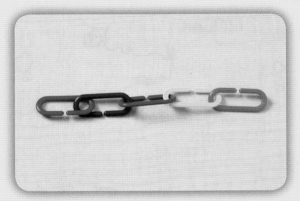

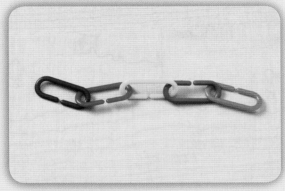

1. Display a chain of Links (red, blue, green, yellow, and orange). Have children make a chain that is exactly the same. Invite children to count aloud with you from one to five, starting with the red Link, as you point to each Link. Then point to each Link as you say the ordinal number aloud, and have children repeat the ordinal number for each Link.

2. Have children make a new chain with blue first, red second, yellow third, green fourth, and orange fifth. Then point to a random color Link in the chain and have children identify the corresponding ordinal number.

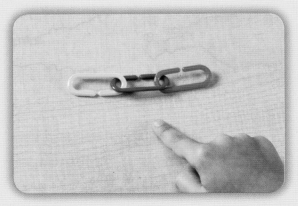

3. Have each child put 3 Links together in any order to make a chain. Then have children explain the order of Links in their chains to their partners. For example, "My chain has yellow first, green second, and orange third."

⚠ Look Out!

Children may be confused about which Link is the beginning and which is the end. Encourage children to work from left to right so that the Link on the far left is first and the Link on the far right is fifth. Remind children that this left to right order is similar to the way they read a sentence. If children are not familiar with the concept of left to right, either help them to use a piece of tape to mark the Link that is first, or have them use only one color (such as red) for the first Link until they understand where the chain begins and ends.

Number and Operations

Counting On

"Counting on" is an important skill for young children to master because it is a prerequisite for understanding addition. Children need to understand that if they begin with a certain number and count on a given number of places, they will reach a larger number.

Objective

Explore "counting on" using a number line.

Skills

- Counting
- Beginning addition
- Estimation

NCTM Expectations

Number and Operations

- Count with understanding and recognize "how many" in sets of objects.
- Develop understanding of the relative position and magnitude of whole numbers and of ordinal and cardinal numbers and their connections.
- Develop a sense of whole numbers and represent and use them in flexible ways, including relating, composing, and decomposing numbers.
- Understand the effects of adding and subtracting whole numbers.
- Develop and use strategies for whole-number computations, with a focus on addition and subtraction.

Try It! *Perform the Try It! activity on the next page.*

Talk About It

Discuss the Try It! activity.

- Display the 0–10 Number Line (BLM 3). **Ask:** *If we start at zero and count to the right* (point to zero and move your finger to the right), *are the numbers getting bigger or smaller? How do you know?*

- **Ask:** *If we start at zero and count up two steps* (point to zero and move your finger to the right until you end up on the number 2), *where do we end up? How do you know?* (Continue this type of questioning with other numbers.)

Solve It

With children, reread the problem. Have children reuse the 0–10 Number Line from the activity to show the eight number jumps that Maya made, starting from zero. Then have them draw a picture next to the number where Maya ended up.

More Ideas

For other ways to teach about "counting on" using a number line—

- Children use 0–10 Number Lines and Three Bear Family® Counters to demonstrate stories about the Bear with at least two sets of steps. For example, **say:** *The Bear started at 3 and took two steps. Then the Bear took one more step.* **Ask:** *Where did it end up?*

- After children have mastered the skill of counting on using a number line, give each child two Backyard Bugs™ grasshoppers and one 0–10 Number Line. Then tell children where the grasshopper started and where it ended up. Have children find out how many numbers the grasshopper jumped.

Standardized Practice

Have children try the following problem.

The rabbit is on the number 1. If the rabbit hops four numbers, where will it land? Draw an X on the number line to show where the rabbit will land.

Try It! 10 minutes | Pairs

Here is a problem demonstrating counting on.

Maya's class is playing a game with a giant number line. They start at zero, a classmate tells them how many numbers to jump, and then they jump and tell where they ended up. Ken told Maya to jump 8 numbers. Where did Maya end up?

Introduce the problem. Then have children do the activity to solve the problem. Distribute Backyard Bugs™ grasshoppers and 0–10 Number Lines (BLM 3) to children.

Materials
- Backyard Bugs™ (1 grasshopper per child)
- 0–10 Number Line (BLM 3; 1 per child)

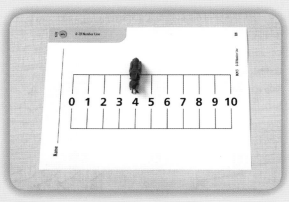

1. Have children place their grasshoppers on zero on their number lines. Then have them show how their grasshoppers jump five numbers. **Say:** *Count as your grasshopper jumps.* **Ask:** *Where did the grasshopper end up after jumping five numbers?*

2. Have children place their grasshoppers on number 1 on their number lines. Then have them show how their grasshoppers jump three numbers. **Say:** *Count as your grasshopper jumps.* **Ask:** *Where did the grasshopper end up after jumping three numbers from number 1?*

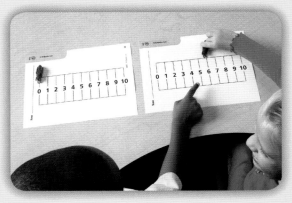

3. Instruct children to work with their partners and take turns telling where the grasshopper should start and how many numbers it should jump. Then have children use the number line to show how many numbers the grasshopper jumped and where it ended up.

⚠ Look Out!

Watch out for children who start their grasshoppers on the number 1 regardless of instructions because they are used to counting by starting with one. Remind children that they must start their grasshoppers on the number you or their partners say and begin counting from that number.

Number and Operations

Part-Part-Whole

One highly effective model for introducing addition is the part-part-whole model. Classroom research has shown that when children are provided with experiences identifying and discussing parts and wholes of quantities, they make fewer errors in deciding when to add in problem situations.

Try It! *Perform the Try It! activity on the next page.*

Talk About It

Discuss the Try It! activity.

- **Ask:** *How many Snap Cubes® are there all together in the train you made? How do you know?*

- **Ask:** *How many Cubes of each color are there?* Repeat this question for different combinations of colors. Make sure that children understand that the different combinations all show the number 5.

- After children have mastered the concept of part-part-whole, encourage them to work with Cubes to discover other smaller parts that make up numbers 2 to 5.

Solve It

With children, reread the problem. Have each child build and draw one way that David and Lisa could put together their Cubes to make a train of five with two different colors. Ask volunteers to share their solutions with the class.

More Ideas

For other ways to teach about part-part-whole—

- Have children write a number from 1 to 5 on a sheet of paper. Ask them to use combinations of the same kind of Backyard Bugs™ in two different colors to show this number. For example, children could use two yellow spiders and two purple spiders to show the number 4. Then have children draw and color the combinations of Bugs that show each number.

- Display a chain of five blue Link 'N' Learn® Links and ask children how many there are. Replace one blue Link with a red Link. Ask children how the group has changed and if there are still five Links. Continue showing other combinations for 5, replacing one more Link each time. Repeat this activity with other combinations of Links to show numbers 1 through 10.

Standardized Practice

Have children try the following problem.

Draw a picture of 4 fish. Make some of the fish red and some of the fish blue.

Objective

Identify a whole number as a combination of two parts.

Skills

- Counting
- Adding
- Using models

NCTM Expectations

Number and Operations
- Develop a sense of whole numbers and represent and use them in flexible ways, including relating, composing, and decomposing numbers.
- Understand the effects of adding and subtracting whole numbers.
- Develop and use strategies for whole-number computations, with a focus on addition and subtraction.
- Use a variety of methods and tools to compute, including objects, mental computation, estimation, paper and pencil, and calculators.

Try It!   15 minutes | Pairs

Here is a problem involving the concept of part-part-whole.

David and Lisa want to make a train of five Snap Cubes® using two different colors. What is one way they can do this?

Introduce the problem. Then have children do the activity to solve the problem.

Distribute Cubes to children.

1. Have children build a train of five Cubes. The Cubes should all be the same color. **Ask:** *How many Cubes are in your train?*

2. Say: *You have made a train of five Cubes that are all the same color. Now let's make a train of five Cubes using two different colors.* Instruct children to remove one Cube from the train they have made and replace it with a Cube of a different color.

3. Have children vary the makeup of their trains by using three of one color and two of the other. Help children understand that all these different combinations make up a total of five.

⚠ Look Out!

Watch for children who don't recognize that the whole group can be made up of different parts. Have children do similar activities using different kinds of manipulatives, such as two colors of Three Bear Family® Counters or two kinds of Backyard Bugs™.

Number and Operations

Joining Problems

Being able to join, or put together, two sets of objects and recognize that the sum of the combined set is greater than either of the sets alone is one of the most important concepts children will learn. In the future, subtraction will be introduced as the opposite of addition, and multiplication will be introduced as repeated addition.

Try It! *Perform the Try It! activity on the next page.*

Talk About It

Discuss the Try It! activity.

- Make sure children understand that joining is the same as putting together or adding two groups. While discussing the activity, emphasize the following terms: *join, put together, add, in all,* and *all together.*
- **Ask:** *When you join or add two groups, how do you find the number in all?*
- **Ask:** *When you join or add two groups, are there more or fewer in the number in all?* **Say:** *Explain how you know.*

Solve It

With children, reread the problem. Have children draw a picture showing 2 children on the swings and 1 child on the slide. Have children number the children in the picture to show that there are a total of 3 children. **Ask:** *How did you find the number of children in all on the playground?*

More Ideas

For other ways to teach about joining problems—

- Have children make chains of 3 blue Link 'N' Learn® Links. Then have them add 3 red Links to the chain. Ask children how they can find the number in all. Repeat with different numbers of Links.
- Have children work with a partner. Have one partner make a train of 3 green Snap Cubes®. Have the other partner make a train of 2 yellow Cubes. Instruct children to join their trains and tell how many Cubes they used to build their trains in all. Repeat with different numbers of Cubes.

Standardized Practice

Have children try the following problem.

There are 2 ducks inside the pond. There are 4 ducks outside the pond. How many ducks are there in all?

Objective

Solve joining problems by combining two groups to make a larger group (part-part-whole addition).

Skills

- Addition
- Computing
- Using models

NCTM Expectations

Number and Operations

- Develop a sense of whole numbers and represent and use them in flexible ways, including relating, composing, and decomposing numbers.
- Understand the effects of adding and subtracting whole numbers.
- Develop and use strategies for whole-number computations, with a focus on addition and subtraction.
- Use a variety of methods and tools to compute, including objects, mental computation, estimation, paper and pencil, and calculators.

Try It! 15 minutes | Independent

Here is a problem about joining two groups together.

There were 2 children playing on the swings at recess. There was 1 child playing on the slide. How many children were on the playground in all?

Introduce the problem. Then have children do the activity to solve the problem. Distribute 5 Three Bear Family® Counters and one copy of the Part-Part-Whole Workmat (BLM 4) to each child.

> **Materials**
> • Three Bear Family® Counters (5 assorted Counters per child)
> • Part-Part-Whole Workmat (BLM 4; 1 per child)

1. Have children put 2 Bear Counters in one of the small parts on their workmats. Then have children put 1 Bear Counter in the other small part on their workmats. Have children count the number of Bear Counters in each small part on their workmats.

2. Instruct children to move all of the Bear Counters from the small parts on their workmats to the large, or whole, area. Invite children to count all of the Bears together in the whole area aloud with you. **Ask:** *How many Bears are there in all?*

3. Have children put 3 Bear Counters in one of the small parts on their workmats and 2 Bear Counters in the other small part. Then have children move all of the Bear Counters together into the whole area on their workmats and count to find the number of Bear Counters in all.

⚠ Look Out!

Children may try to tell the number of Bears in only one of the groups. Remind children that they must join, or put together, the groups in the large section and count all of the Bears to find how many there are in all.

Using the Plus Sign

Children must learn to recognize the plus sign and recall that it indicates addition. When solving word problems, the plus sign might not be present. Because of this, children need to learn that words and phrases, such as *join, put together, add, in all,* and *all together,* are clues to addition.

Try It! *Perform the Try It! activity on the next page.*

Talk About It

Discuss the Try It! activity.

- During your discussion, emphasize the following terms that indicate addition: *join, put together, add, in all,* and *all together.*

- Display a plus sign. **Ask:** *What do we call this sign? What does the plus sign tell you to do? How do you know when to use the plus sign?*

- **Say:** *Martin has 4 blocks. Tina has 2 blocks.* **Ask:** *How many blocks do they have in all? What do the words "in all" tell you to do? What numbers would you use to show this problem?* Have children write the addition sentence.

Solve It

With children, reread the problem. Give each child a new copy of the Part-Part-Whole Workmat (BLM 4). Tell children to draw 3 green books in one "part" and 2 yellow books in the other "part." Have children draw a plus sign between the two groups. Then have children draw 3 green and 2 yellow books in the "whole" section and count to find the number in all.

More Ideas

For other ways to teach about using the plus sign—

- Draw two large squares with a plus sign between them on a piece of construction paper. Have children use this as a workmat to solve addition problems with Backyard Bugs™. Introduce a simple problem, such as "Tony found 3 spiders and 1 caterpillar. How many bugs did he find in all?"

- Using the above workmat, two colors of Snap Cubes®, and one set of Number Cards 0–5 (BLM 1) per pair, have children make up and solve addition problems. Each child will pick a Number Card and place that number of their color of Cubes in one of the squares on the mat. Together, they will join the groups to make a train and count the total number of Cubes.

Standardized Practice

Have children try the following problem.

Draw a plus sign between the two circles.
Write the number of stars in all.

Objective

Identify the plus sign and use it to show addition.

Skills

- Addition
- Writing numerals
- Using models

NCTM Expectations

Number and Operations
- Understand various meanings of addition and subtraction of whole numbers and the relationship between the two operations.
- Understand the effects of adding and subtracting whole numbers.
- Use a variety of methods and tools to compute, including objects, mental computation, estimation, paper and pencil, and calculators.

Algebra
- Model situations that involve the addition and subtraction of whole numbers using objects, pictures, and symbols.

Try It!   15 minutes | Independent

Here is a problem involving addition using the plus sign.

Makayla's teacher read 3 stories to the class before snack time. After recess, her teacher read 2 stories. How can Makayla find the number of stories her teacher read in all?

Introduce the problem. Then have children do the activity to solve the problem. First, have children stand up and hold their arms out to the sides to form a plus sign with their bodies. Draw a plus sign on the board and encourage children to practice drawing the plus sign. Explain that the plus sign shows us when to join things, or add. Make sure to introduce and discuss the many words and phrases used to indicate addition. Next, distribute 1" Color Cubes and Part-Part-Whole Workmats (BLM 4) to children.

Materials
- 1" Color Cubes (10 assorted cubes per child)
- Part-Part-Whole Workmat (BLM 4; 1 per child)

1. **Say:** _Listen to this problem. I had 3 cubes. Then I found 2 cubes._ **Ask:** _How many cubes do I have in all?_ Have children place 3 cubes in one of the small part sections of the workmat. Then have children place 2 cubes in the other small part section.

2. After children have placed the cubes in the small part sections, have them write the number for each group in each of the sections. **Ask:** _What do the words "in all" in the problem tell us to do? What does the plus sign tell us to do?_ Have children draw a plus sign between the two part sections on their workmats.

⚠ Look Out!

Watch for children who are having trouble understanding the connection between the plus sign and addition. Demonstrate additional joining problems using the plus sign for these children.

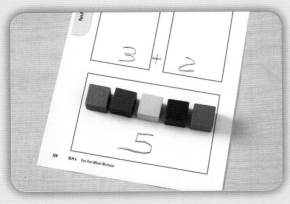

3. Instruct children to move all of the cubes into the large, whole section. Then have children count to find the number in all. Have children write this number in the whole section. **Say:** _This is the number in all._ Repeat the activity with other addition problems.

Number and Operations

Decomposing Numbers

In order to become fluent in math and feel comfortable manipulating numbers, children must find flexible and creative ways to break apart, or decompose, numbers to form equivalent representations. For example, knowing that 4 can be represented as 3 + 1 or 2 + 2 enables children to think of 7 + 4 as 7 + 3 + 1 or 7 + 2 + 2.

Objective

Decompose numbers to find different representations of the same number.

Skills

- Counting
- Subtraction
- Writing numerals

NCTM Expectations

Number and Operations
- Develop a sense of whole numbers and represent and use them in flexible ways, including relating, composing, and decomposing numbers.
- Understand various meanings of addition and subtraction of whole numbers and the relationship between the two operations.
- Understand the effects of adding and subtracting whole numbers.

Try It! *Perform the Try It! activity on the next page.*

Talk About It

Discuss the Try It! activity.

- Display the two complete trains used for the activity. **Ask:** *How many Snap Cubes® are in each train? How are the trains different?* **Say:** *Even though the trains are made up of different numbers of red and blue Cubes, both trains have 5 Cubes in all.*

- Display the train from Step 2. **Ask:** *How many red Cubes? How many blue Cubes?* (Point to the expression 1 + 4 as you ask children to repeat after you.) **Say:** *This train of 5 Cubes is made of 1 red Cube and 4 blue Cubes. 1 plus 4 is 5.*

- Display the train from Step 3. **Ask:** *How many red Cubes? How many blue Cubes?* (Point to the expression 2 + 3 as you ask children to repeat after you.) **Say:** *This train of 5 Cubes is made of 2 red Cubes and 3 blue Cubes. 2 plus 3 is 5.*

Solve It

With children, reread the problem. Then have children draw pictures to show at least two ways the 5 games can be put into the two game drawers. Encourage children to share and discuss their drawings with their classmates.

More Ideas

For other ways to teach about decomposing numbers—

- After children have mastered decomposing numbers from 2 through 5, have them complete the same Try It! activity with Snap Cubes using numbers from 6 through 10.

- Have children work in pairs. Instruct one child in each pair to use two different colors of Snap Cubes and put together a specific number of Cubes in random order. Then tell the other child in each pair to separate the Cubes and make one train for each color while completing this sentence: _____ plus _____ is _____ .

Standardized Practice

Have children try the following problem.

Carl has 4 carrot sticks. He piled them this way. Draw another way Carl can pile his carrot sticks.

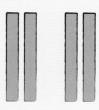

Try It! 30 minutes | Pairs

Here is a problem about decomposing the number 5.

During classroom cleanup time, it's Jodi's job to put the 5 classroom games in the two game drawers. How can Jodi find the number of different ways she can put the 5 games in the game drawers?

Introduce the problem. Then have children do the activity to solve the problem. Distribute 10 Snap Cubes® to each pair of children.

Materials
• Snap Cubes® (5 red and 5 blue Cubes per pair)

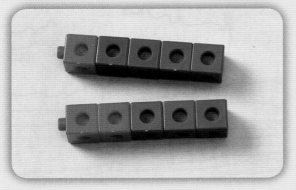

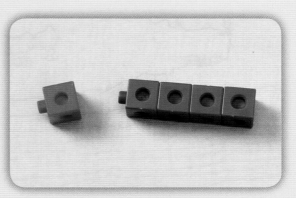

1. Instruct children to make two 5-Cube trains (one is made of 1 red and 4 blue Cubes and the other is made of 2 red and 3 blue Cubes). Then have children compare the trains. Guide children to the conclusion that the trains have the same number of Cubes (5), but each train has a different number of red and blue Cubes. Write the number 5 on the chalkboard.

2. Display the train with 1 red Cube and 4 blue Cubes. Instruct children to break this train apart by removing the red Cube. Help children to recognize that the train of 1 red Cube and the train of 4 blue Cubes together made up 5 Cubes. Below the number 5 on the chalkboard, write 1 + 4.

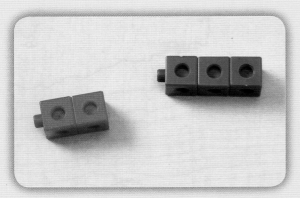

3. Display the train of 2 red Cubes and 3 blue Cubes. Have children break this train apart into two trains. Help children to recognize that the train of 2 red Cubes and the train of 3 blue Cubes together made up 5 Cubes. Below 1 + 4 on the chalkboard, write 2 + 3. Encourage children to see if they can find other ways to break 5 into groups.

⚠ Look Out!

Watch for children who are having a difficult time understanding that a number can be made of and broken apart into two groups in different ways. Have these children work with a set of 5 Cubes that are all the same color. This way, children will be able to see that no matter how they break their set of 5 Cubes apart (1 + 4 or 2 + 3), they always make up a train of 5 Cubes.

Number and Operations

Separating Problems

When we begin with a group and separate, or take away, a portion of that group and count up what is left, we are subtracting. The separating method of subtraction is an important beginning strategy that will help children as they develop fluency with single-digit number combinations.

Try It! *Perform the Try It! activity on the next page.*

Talk About It

Discuss the Try It! activity.

- **Ask:** *After you take away from a number, is the number you are left with more or fewer? How do you know?*
- **Say:** *Look at your Take-Away Workmat (BLM 5). Think about how you use your workmat to solve a take away problem.* **Ask:** *What do you put in the big circle? What do you put in the small circle? How do you find the number that is left?*

Solve It

With children, reread the problem. Have children reuse the Take-Away Workmat from the Try It! activity. Have children make a drawing to show the number of Three Bear Family® Counters the teacher took away (2 Bears) from the 5 Bears on the shelf in the small (take away) circle. Then have children draw the Bears that were left on the shelf in the big circle. Encourage children to use their drawings to explain how they solved the problem.

More Ideas

For other ways to teach about subtraction—

- Have the class work together to use Backyard Bugs™ or other counters to compose and then solve a separating story problem.
- Have pairs of children place 5 Backyard Bugs in a paper bag. Instruct one child to take away some of the Bugs from the bag. Have children count to find the number of Bugs that were taken away. Then encourage children to work together to figure out how many Bugs are left in the bag. Finally, have children check to see if they were correct by counting the Bugs left inside the bag. Encourage children to compete the following sentence: [number] Bugs take away [number] Bugs is [number] Bugs. For example, 5 Bugs take away 3 Bugs is 2 Bugs. Repeat the activity with different numbers of Bugs.

Standardized Practice

Have children try the following problem.

Jamal brought 3 stickers to school to share with his friend Mark. Jamal gave 1 sticker to Mark. Draw a picture to show how many stickers Jamal has left.

Objective

Solve separating problems by taking away one group from a larger group and counting what is left.

Skills

- Subtraction
- Counting
- Using models

NCTM Expectations

Number and Operations
- Understand various meanings of addition and subtraction of whole numbers and the relationship between the two operations.
- Understand the effects of adding and subtracting whole numbers.
- Develop and use strategies for whole-number computations, with a focus on addition and subtraction.
- Use a variety of methods and tools to compute, including objects, mental computation, estimation, paper and pencil, and calculators.

Try It! 20 minutes | Independent

Here is a separating problem.

Rico's teacher put 5 teddy bears on the shelf. Then she took 2 teddy bears away and put them in a basket. How many teddy bears were left on the shelf?

Introduce the problem. Then have children do the activity to solve the problem. Distribute 1 copy of the Take-Away Workmat (BLM 5) and 5 Three Bear Family® Counters to each child.

Materials
- Three Bear Family® Counters (5 per child)
- Take-Away Workmat (BLM 5; 1 per child)

1. Instruct children to place all of their Bear Counters in the big circle on the Take-Away Workmat. Have children count the Bears aloud with you one at a time and identify that there are 5 Bears in all in the big circle.

2. Have children take 2 Bears away from the big circle and follow the arrow to move them into the small circle.

3. Instruct children to count the Bears that are left in the big circle aloud with you. Then help children to understand that 5 take away 2 is 3.

⚠ Look Out!

Watch for children who are having a difficult time figuring out which number of Counters to move into the take away (small) circle on the workmat. Remind children that the number of Counters that should be placed in the small circle is the number that should be taken away from the group they started with.

Objective

Identify the minus sign and use it to show subtraction.

Skills

- Subtraction
- Counting
- Using models

NCTM Expectations

Number and Operations
- Understand various meanings of addition and subtraction of whole numbers and the relationship between the two operations.
- Understand the effects of adding and subtracting whole numbers.
- Develop and use strategies for whole-number computations, with a focus on addition and subtraction.
- Use a variety of methods and tools to compute, including objects, mental computation, estimation, paper and pencil, and calculators.

Number and Operations

Using the Minus Sign

The minus sign is used to show subtraction. Children must learn how to recognize the minus sign. They also must learn to remember what operation it signifies. Often, word problems will not use the minus sign. Because of this, it is important that children learn that words like *less, fewer, take away,* and *minus* indicate subtraction.

Try It! *Perform the Try It! activity on the next page.*

Talk About It

Discuss the Try It! activity.

- During the activity discussion, emphasize that the words *fewer, less,* and *take away* all tell about using the minus sign.
- **Ask:** *When we take away from a group, does the new group have more or less? How do you know?*
- Instruct children to look at their Take-Away Workmats (BLM 5). Point to the minus sign on a workmat. **Ask:** *What do we call this sign? What does the minus sign show? What should you do when you see the minus sign? When you use the minus sign, are you left with more or fewer than you started with?*

Solve It

With children, reread the problem. Have children make a drawing to show the number of ladybugs that Maria saw at first (5). Then have children draw the ladybugs that flew away (3). Ask children to draw the minus sign between the two groups. Then have them draw how many ladybugs were left underneath.

More Ideas

For other ways to teach about using the minus sign—

- Write simple subtraction problems using the minus sign on the chalkboard, on large sheets of paper, or on note cards. Then have children act out the problems with Three Bear Family® Counters.
- Create a workmat by drawing two large squares with a minus sign between them on a piece of construction paper. Give children a problem such as, "Dana had four crayons on her desk. She put one back in the box. How many crayons were left on Dana's desk?" Have children practice using Snap Cubes®, or crayons, to show the problem on the workmat.

Standardized Practice

Have children try the following problem.

Tanya had 6 circles. She gave 4 circles to Chris. How many circles does Tanya have left? Draw a minus sign between the two groups. Draw the number of circles left.

Try It! 20 minutes | Independent

Here is a problem that demonstrates using the minus sign.

During recess, Maria found five ladybugs on the playground. Then three of the ladybugs flew away. How many ladybugs were left on the playground?

Introduce the problem. Then have children do the activity to solve the problem. Distribute one copy of the Take-Away Workmat (BLM 5) and five Backyard Bugs™ to each child.

Materials
- Backyard Bugs™ (5 per child)
- Take-Away Workmat (BLM 5; 1 per child)
- paper (1 sheet per child)

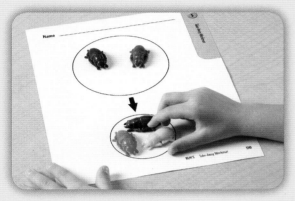

1. Say: *I had five Bugs. I took away three Bugs.* **Ask:** *How many Bugs were left?* Instruct children to place all of their Bugs in the big circle on the Take-Away Workmat. Have children take three Bugs away from the big circle and follow the arrow to move them into the small circle.

2. Introduce the minus sign. Draw a minus sign on the chalkboard or on a sheet of paper and display it for children. Tell children that the minus sign describes what they did when they took three Bugs away from the five Bugs in the large circle. Have children write a minus sign between the two circles on their workmats. Tell children that when we use the minus sign we are taking away. This means that we will have *fewer* or *less* than we started out with.

3. On the chalkboard or on a sheet of paper, draw the problem using five Bugs, a minus sign, and three Bugs. Then write 5 − 3. Explain that this is how we would write the problem children just did. Make sure children understand that the two expressions show the same problem. Have children practice drawing and writing the corresponding expression.

⚠ Look Out!

Watch for children who have trouble understanding the connection between the minus sign and the following vocabulary terms: *fewer, less,* and *take away.* Emphasize these words for children as you provide additional examples of subtraction problems. Also, watch for children who confuse the plus sign with the minus sign. Remind children that the minus sign tells us to take away and the plus sign tells us to put together.

Number and Operations

Identifying Halves

Identifying that a whole is made up of parts, two equal parts make up one whole, and two equal parts are called halves is at the foundation of understanding fractions and division. It is important that children recognize that the two equal parts are the same size and shape.

Objective

Identify halves as two equal parts of a region.

Skills

- Fractions
- Division
- Comparing

NCTM Expectations

Number and Operations
- Understand and represent commonly used fractions, such as $\frac{1}{4}$, $\frac{1}{3}$, and $\frac{1}{2}$.
- Understand situations that entail multiplication and division, such as equal groupings of objects and sharing equally.

Try It! *Perform the Try It! activity on the next page.*

Talk About It

Discuss the Try It! activity.

- **Ask:** *Which is bigger: one part of the Pattern Block or the whole block?*
- **Say:** *Remember, when two parts are exactly the same size and shape, we call them equal parts. Two equal parts that make a whole shape are called halves.*
- **Say:** *Look at your Pattern Blocks Recording Sheet (BLM 6).* **Ask:** *What block did you use to make two equal parts or halves for the blue block? The yellow block?*

Solve It

With children, reread the problem. Then have children draw a picture to show how Mr. Grove can split up the table so that two children can each use an equal part.

More Ideas

For other ways to teach about equal parts and halves—

- Give each child a blank sheet of paper and an assortment of Attribute Blocks (triangles, squares, rectangles, and hexagons). Have children arrange two of the same shape of block on the sheet of paper to create one large shape. Instruct children to use a crayon to trace around their shapes, or trace around the large shape for children. Then ask children to trade shape papers with another classmate and use blocks to split the whole shape into the correct number of equal parts.

- After children have mastered the concept of halves, encourage them to explore different numbers of equal parts with Pattern Blocks by finding out how many of the same equal parts (green triangles) they would use to make one blue block (two green triangles), one red block (three green triangles), and one yellow block (six green triangles).

Standardized Practice

Have children try the following problem.

Color half of the circle green.

Try It! 30 minutes | Pairs

Here is a problem about identifying two equal parts or halves.

There is a table in Mr. Grove's classroom that is shaped like a yellow Pattern Block. How can Mr. Grove split up the table so that two children can each use an equal part?

Introduce the problem. Then have children do the activity to solve the problem. Distribute Pattern Blocks Recording Sheets (BLM 6) and blocks to children.

Materials
- Pattern Blocks (2 of each shape block per pair)
- Pattern Blocks Recording Sheet (BLM 6; 1 per child)
- crayons

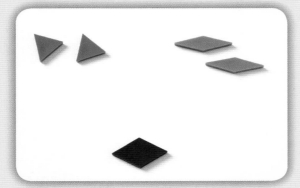

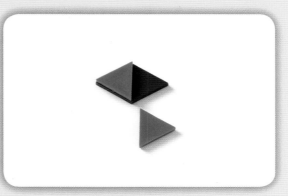

1. Have children find the blue block. Explain that the blue block is one whole. Tell children that a whole can be split into parts, and a part is smaller than one whole. Have children find the blocks that are smaller (green) or thinner (tan) than the blue block. Have children compare each of these blocks to the blue block. **Say:** *If you put two of these blocks together, you will have a block that is the same size and shape as the blue block.*

2. Have children put two of each shape together (green triangle and tan rhombus), side to side. Instruct children to compare each of the larger shapes. **Ask:** *Which two blocks together are the same size and shape as the blue block?* Encourage children to put the two green blocks on top of the blue block to completely cover it, and then remove one block. **Say:** *Two green blocks together make up one blue block. One green block is half of a blue block.*

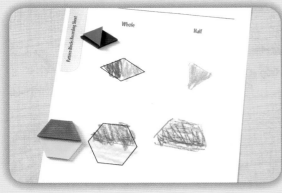

⚠ Look Out!

Encourage children who are having trouble covering each shape with other shapes to show equal parts to use two green triangles to "build" the blue block and then separate it to see that each triangle is an equal part. These children should repeat the above step with the red and yellow blocks.

3. Have children find the block that is half of the yellow block (red trapezoid). Then encourage children to complete their recording sheets. Have children draw the block shape that is half of each whole block shape.

Geometry

Geometry in the elementary grades allows children to learn about geometric shapes and structures and to analyze their characteristics and relationships. Spatial visualization is an important aspect of this learning. Through hands-on experiences, children learn to build and manipulate mental representations of geometric figures. These geometric skills and ideas are useful in determining area, identifying fractions, interpreting data, understanding algebra, and solving real-world problems.

Elementary-level geometry focuses on the properties of geometric figures and their relationships to one another. Children learn about these properties through manipulation of concrete materials. Problem-solving skills are encouraged through the use of visual and coordinate representations.

The Grades Pre-K–2 NCTM Standards for Geometry suggest that children should:

- Analyze characteristics and properties of two- and three-dimensional geometric shapes and develop mathematical arguments about geometric relationships
- Specify locations and describe spatial relationships using coordinate geometry and other representational systems
- Apply transformations and use symmetry to analyze mathematical situations
- Use visualization, spatial reasoning, and geometric modeling to solve problems

---

Young children bring geometric and spatial knowledge with them when they begin school. Through explorations, investigations, and discussions, teachers can refine and expand upon this knowledge. Children develop spatial visualization skills through building and manipulating concrete shapes. This ability can then be extended to mental representations of shapes, relationships, and transformations. The following are activities involving manipulatives that children can use to develop skills in **Geometry.**

Geometry

Contents

Geometry

Left and Right

The relative position of any object can be described using the words *right* and *left*. As with other ways of determining location, such as *inside* and *outside*, *right* and *left* require a reference point. Without something on the right, there is no left. Without something on the left, there is no right. The ability to describe location in terms of left and right is important in building geometric thinking and is especially useful in real life. Using the vocabulary of right and left will help children describe locations in space.

Try It! *Perform the Try It! activity on the next page.*

Talk About It

Discuss the Try It! activity.

■ **Ask:** *How do you know which is left and which is right?* Discuss with students how they remember left and right, for example by using their left and right hands.

■ **Ask:** *Can you think of some ways to remember the difference between left and right?* Discuss ways to remember left and right, such as placing the left hand palm down to form the letter *L* with the index finger and thumb.

■ **Ask:** *How did you know where to put the yellow and green Color Tiles? How did you know where to put the blue and red tiles?*

Solve It

With children, reread the problem. Ask children to set a plain piece of paper in front of them. Have them use crayons or markers to draw yellow and green circles to show the paints on the left side. Then ask them to draw red and blue circles on the right side.

More Ideas

For other ways to teach about *right* and *left*—

■ Ask children to separate Backyard Bugs™ into two groups. Bugs with four legs should go on the left. Bugs with more than four legs should go on the right.

■ Have children use two sheets of paper and Attribute Blocks to practice following directions that involve left and right. Students should have two sheets of paper in front of them, one on the right and one on the left. Tell them to put a red triangle on the left sheet of paper, a blue rectangle on the right sheet of paper, and so on.

Standardized Practice

Have children try the following problem.

Draw a triangle on the left side of the box.
Then draw a circle on the right side of the box.

Objective

Identify *left* and *right*.

Skills

• Describing relative positions
• Classifying location
• Spatial reasoning

NCTM Expectations

Geometry
• Describe, name, and interpret relative positions in space and apply ideas about relative position.

Try It! 20 minutes | Groups of 3

Here is a problem demonstrating *right* and *left*.

After an art project, Mr. Lewis wants the paints to be put away. He wants the green and yellow paints to be put on the left side of the drawer. He wants the red and blue paints to be put on the right side of the drawer. Can you draw how Mr. Lewis wants the paints to be put away?

Introduce the problem. Then have children do the activity to solve the problem.

Distribute Color Tiles and Sorting Circles to groups of children.

Materials
- Color Tiles (several per group with at least 1 of each color)
- Sorting Circles (2 per group)

1. Help children understand the concept of right and left by using the right and left sides of their bodies. **Say:** *Raise your right hand. Now touch your left knee with your left hand.* Make sure children are able to identify left and right correctly.

2. Say: *We can use our right hand to help us know when something is on the right side. We can use our left hand to help us know when something is on the left.* Instruct children to place one circle in front of the right of their group and one circle in front of the left of their group.

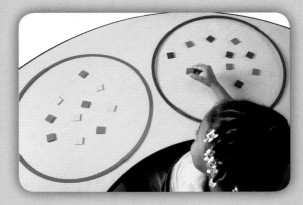

3. Invite children to place green and yellow tiles in the left circle. Remind children that this is the circle to the left of their group. Have children place red and blue tiles in right circle. Remind them that this is the circle to the right of their group.

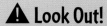

⚠ Look Out!

If children need extra help remembering right and left, spend some time discussing the importance of right and left in children's everyday life. Point out that we read from left to right, or that the school bus driver sits on the left side of the bus. Look around the classroom and have children practice identifying objects that are on their right or left. Also, point out to children that right/left position is relative to their position.

Objective

Explore attributes of plane shapes.

Skills

- Shape recognition
- Describing attributes
- Comparing shapes

NCTM Expectations

Geometry
- Recognize, name, build, draw, compare, and sort two- and three-dimensional shapes.
- Describe attributes and parts of two- and three-dimensional shapes.

Geometry

Attributes of Plane Shapes

Each plane shape has attributes that make it unique and recognizable. A *square* has four equal sides and four corners. A *rectangle* also has four sides. However, a rectangle has two opposite sides that are long and two opposite sides that are short. A *triangle* has three sides and three corners. A *circle* is a plane shape that has no sides or corners. Size and color are also attributes. Learning the basic attributes of plane shapes introduces children to shape and attribute vocabulary and prepares children for more advanced skills in geometry and algebra, such as sorting and classifying.

Try It! *Perform the Try It! activity on the next page.*

Talk About It

Discuss the Try It! activity.

- Hold up a square. **Ask:** *What shape is this? How many sides does it have? How many corners does it have?*

- Hold up a rectangle. **Ask:** *What shape is this? How many sides does it have? How many corners? Is it the same as the first shape, or is it different?*

- Hold up a triangle. **Ask:** *What shape is this? How many sides does it have? How many corners?*

- Hold up a circle. **Ask:** *What shape is this? How many sides does it have? How many corners?*

Solve It

With children, reread the problem. Have children draw the shapes that Nicky and Louisa drew on a piece of paper. Have them write the number of sides each shape has next to the shape. Ask children what shapes they have drawn. Discuss with children how they can tell that the shapes are different.

More Ideas

For other ways to teach about the attributes of plane shapes—

- Have children sort Pattern Blocks by color, number of sides, or number of corners. Ask them to identify the shapes they know.

- Have children work in pairs with Attribute Blocks to describe how two shapes are alike and how they are different. For example, give a pair of children a red square and a yellow rectangle and have them tell two ways the shapes are the same and two ways the shapes are different.

Standardized Practice

Have children try the following problem.

Draw a line from one shape to the shape that matches it.

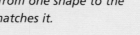

Try It! 40 minutes | Groups of 3

Here is a problem demonstrating attributes of plane shapes.

Nicky and Louisa are drawing shapes on the chalkboard. Nicky draws a shape that has four sides. All the sides are the same length. Louisa draws a shape that has three sides. What shapes did Nicky and Louisa draw? Are the shapes the same or different? How can you tell?

Introduce the problem. Then have children do the activity to solve the problem.

Distribute bags filled with several matching pairs of Attribute Blocks to each group.

Materials
- Attribute Blocks (several squares, rectangles, triangles, and circles per group)
- paper grocery bags or pillow cases (1 per group)

1. Have children close their eyes, reach into the bag, and pull out a block. Children should say the name of the shape they chose and note how many sides and corners it has.

2. Next, children should reach into the bag and try to find a shape that matches the first block they chose. Have children count to make sure that the two blocks have the same number of sides and corners. **Ask:** *Are the two shapes the same?*

⚠ Look Out!

Some children may confuse the shapes, especially the rectangle and the square. If this happens, show a square and talk about how all sides are the same. Then lay the square on top of a rectangle and point out that the rectangle has two long sides and two short sides.

3. Finally, have children put their shapes back in the bag and pick out two new blocks that are different from each other. They should count the number of sides and corners and name the shapes.

Geometry

Plane Shapes and Real-Life Objects

Recognition of basic plane shapes is a fundamental geometry skill. The ability to identify circles, squares, triangles, and rectangles and to compare them to real-life objects helps children to become more familiar with the specific attributes of a variety of plane shapes.

Try It! *Perform the Try It! activity on the next page.*

Talk About It

Discuss the Try It! activity.

- **Ask:** *How is a roll of tape the same as a circle? Different from a circle?*
- **Say:** *Explain how you know whether or not the things you see are shaped like a circle, square, rectangle, or triangle.*
- **Ask:** *What things are shaped like a circle? Like a square? Like a rectangle? Like a triangle?*

Solve It

With children, reread the problem. Give each child four blank sheets of paper and crayons. Have children draw one real-life object for each plane shape.

More Ideas

For other ways to teach about plane shapes—

- Give each pair of children four Attribute Blocks (circle, square, triangle, and rectangle) and an assortment of pictures of real-life objects that are shaped like plane shapes. Have children compare the block shapes to the pictures. Have them identify the real-life objects that are shaped like plane shapes. Then have children sort the pictures and pile them under the matching block shapes.

- Use Attribute Blocks to play a guessing game with children. Hold up a block shape and give children clues about a real-life object in the classroom and have them identify the object. For example, hold up a block rectangle and **say:** *I am shaped like a rectangle and I have pages that you can read. What am I?* (a book)

Standardized Practice

Have children try the following problem.

Color the picture that looks like a circle red. Color the picture that looks like a square yellow. Color the picture that looks like a rectangle green.

Objective

Identify circles, squares, rectangles, and triangles and compare them to real-life objects.

Skills

- Comparing
- Sorting
- Modeling

NCTM Expectations

Geometry
- Recognize, name, build, draw, compare, and sort two- and three-dimensional shapes.
- Recognize geometric shapes and structures in the environment and specify their location.

Try It!   30 minutes | Groups of 4

Here is a problem about plane shapes and real-life objects.

As Amanda looked around her classroom, she wondered . . . What things that we see are shaped like circles? What things that we see are shaped like squares? What things that we see are shaped like rectangles? What things that we see are shaped like triangles?

Introduce the problem. Then have children do the activity to solve the problem. First, look around the classroom to make sure that there are a variety of objects shaped like circles, squares, triangles, and rectangles. If there are not, then either draw a variety of simple objects on the chalkboard or cut pictures of real-life objects out of a magazine or newspaper to display to children. Then distribute Attribute Blocks and Sorting Circles to each group.

Materials
- Attribute Blocks (2 or 3 of each shape—circle, square, rectangle, and triangle—per group)
- Sorting Circles (2 per group)

1. Make sure that there is a roll of tape or other common real-life circular-shaped object in the classroom. Have children look at the roll of tape. Then encourage children to examine their blocks. **Ask:** *What shape does a roll of tape look like?* (a circle) Then have children compare the block circle to the roll of tape.

2. Point to a classroom object shaped like a square. Have children find the matching block and compare the block to the object. Have children decide which Sorting Circle is for circles and which is for squares and place blocks to represent objects in the appropriate Sorting Circles. Encourage children to find additional examples of circle- and square-shaped real-life objects. Then have children clear their Sorting Circles.

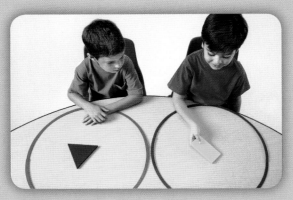

3. Repeat the activity for rectangles and triangles. Have children find examples of rectangle- and triangle-shaped real-life objects, compare them to the block shapes, and sort them into two Sorting Circles.

⚠ Look Out!

Watch for children who are having a difficult time seeing plane shapes in three-dimensional objects. Ask children questions about number of sides, number of corners, and length of sides. Help children to recognize that although an object is much larger or smaller than the block plane shape, it can still have a similar shape.

Geometry

Exploring Shape Attributes

Geometry in the early grades begins with describing the attributes of shapes. Attributes, such as the number of sides and corners a shape has, help children tell different shapes apart. As children become familiar with shapes and their attributes, they construct a framework for understanding not only their spatial world but also other topics in mathematics and in art, science, and social studies.

Try It! *Perform the Try It! activity on the next page.*

Talk About It

Discuss the Try It! activity.

■ **Say:** *Point to a corner of the square. Now point to a side.* **Ask:** *How many sides does a square have? How many corners?*

■ **Ask:** *When you put a Bear in each corner of the triangle, how many Bears did you use? How many sides does a triangle have? How many corners?*

■ **Ask:** *Why couldn't you put a Bear in the corner of a circle? Why couldn't you put a Bear on the side of a circle?*

Solve It

With children, reread the problem. Have children find the Attribute Blocks that Miguel picked out. Then have them trace the blocks on a piece of paper.

More Ideas

■ Have children identify sides and corners in Pattern Blocks. Have them position several blocks on a piece of paper. Then, have them write the number of sides and the number of corners next to each shape.

■ Have children draw shapes using Attribute Blocks as models. For example, tell children to choose a shape with three sides and three corners and then draw a picture of it. Then repeat with other shapes.

Standardized Practice

Have children try the following problem.

Circle the shape that has four sides. Draw an X on the shape with three corners.

Objective

Explore shape attributes and spatial sense.

Skills

• Naming shapes
• Describing shapes
• Comparing attributes

NCTM Expectations

Geometry
• Recognize, name, build, draw, compare, and sort two- and three-dimensional shapes.
• Describe attributes and parts of two- and three-dimensional shapes.
• Create mental images of geometric shapes using spatial memory and spatial visualization.

Try It!   30 minutes | Pairs

Here is a problem about shape attributes and spatial sense.

Miguel and Felicia are making shape collages in class using paper cutouts of Attribute Blocks. Felicia wants to use only shapes with four corners and four sides. Miguel finds two shapes for Felicia to use. Which shapes are they?

Introduce the problem. Then have children do the activity to solve the problem.

To begin, give each pair of children blocks and five Three Bear Family® Counters.

Materials
- Attribute Blocks (1 of each shape per pair)
- Three Bear Family® Counters (5 assorted Bears per pair)

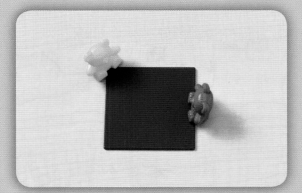

1. Hold up the large square block. Point out that it has four sides and four corners. **Say:** *Put a Bear on one of the sides.* Make sure children are able to place Bears correctly. **Say:** *Now put a Bear in one of the corners.* Watch to see that children put Bear Counters in a corner.

2. Hold up the large triangle block. Point out that it has three corners and three sides. **Say:** *With your partner, put a Bear in each corner of the triangle.* Make sure children correctly identify the corners of the triangles by placing Bear Counters in them.

⚠ Look Out!

Some children may think that placing a Bear somewhere on the perimeter of the circle is the same as placing a Bear on the side. Make sure that children understand that a side is straight, and that circles do not have sides.

3. Now hold up a circle. **Ask:** *Can you put a Bear in a corner of this shape? Can you put a Bear on a side of the shape?* Tell children that they cannot do either of these things because the circle has no sides and no corners.

Geometry

Shape Attribute Riddles

Analyzing characteristics of geometric shapes through hands-on exploration builds a foundation of spatial understanding. By solving riddles involving shape attributes, students will learn to associate abstract concepts of spatial sense with concrete materials like the manipulatives in this lesson.

Objective

Use shape attributes and spatial sense to solve shape riddles.

Skills

- Shape recognition
- Attributes of shapes
- Spatial sense

NCTM Expectations

Geometry
- Recognize, name, build, draw, compare, and sort two- and three-dimensional shapes.

Try It! *Perform the Try It! activity on the next page.*

Talk About It

Discuss the Try It! activity.

- **Ask:** *How can we tell what is the same and what is different about Attribute Block shapes?* Invite children to list the attributes, such as number of corners and sides, size, thickness, and color.

- Discuss with children how they were able to figure out the riddles for other shapes. Be sure that children are discussing the shapes using the words *side* and *corner,* as well as listing the sizes and colors of the blocks.

- **Ask:** *What is the first shape in the line of shapes I described? How do you know? What is the second shape? The third?* Be sure children are putting the shapes in order from left to right.

Solve It

With children, reread the problem. Then have children find the block that Mrs. Chou was thinking of in the problem. Have children draw the block, write the number of corners and sides (0 and 0), and color the shape to match the block.

More Ideas

For other ways to teach about shape attributes—

- Have children work in pairs. One child closes his or her eyes while the other chooses and hides an Attribute Block shape. The other child quizzes the partner about the shape's attributes and tries to guess which shape it is.

- Have children work in pairs. One child sorts Attribute Blocks or Pattern Blocks by a chosen attribute. The other child then guesses which attribute was used to sort the shapes.

Standardized Practice

Have children try the following problem.

Circle the shape that is small, blue, and has three sides and three corners.

Try It! 20 minutes | Groups of 6

Here is a problem about solving shape riddles.

Mrs. Chou asked her class to guess which Attribute Block shape she was thinking of. She said it was small, thick, and red. It had no sides and no corners. What shape was Mrs. Chou thinking of?

Introduce the problem. Then have children do the activity to solve the problem.

Distribute blocks to children. Make sure children identify the different numbers of sides and corners and the different sizes, colors, and thicknesses. Tell children that they are going to play guessing games with the blocks.

Materials
• Attribute Blocks (1 set per group)

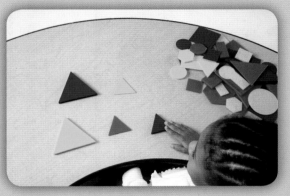

1. Say: *I am a block with three sides and three corners.* **Ask:** *What shape block am I?* Have children narrow down which blocks you might be talking about. They should pick out the triangles from the other blocks.

2. Say: *I am also big, thick, and yellow.* **Ask:** *Which block am I?* Children should hold up the large thick yellow triangle. Repeat steps 1 and 2 for other shapes, sizes, colors, and thicknesses.

3. Say: *I am thinking of a line of two shapes. The first one is small, thin, and blue. It has no sides or corners. The second one is large, thin, and red. It has four sides and four corners. It is not a rectangle.* Children should line up the small blue circle and large red square. Repeat the activity with different orders of shapes.

⚠ Look Out!

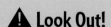

Some children may need a review of ordinal positions before they are able to do step 3 of the activity. To help children remember ordinals, start out by putting three blocks in a line. Using blocks with only one differing attribute will help focus children's attention on the positions of the blocks. Point at the blocks in order, and **say:** *The circle is first in line. The square is second,* and so on.

6

Geometry

Cubes and Spheres

In mathematics, three-dimensional figures are also called *solids.* If something is three-dimensional, it is considered to have many dimensions; it is lifelike. A *cube* is a three-dimensional figure made up of six matching square sides, or two-dimensional shapes. A *sphere* is a three-dimensional figure having all of its points the same distance from its center. As children learn to describe solids, they will develop spatial reasoning and a greater understanding of geometric concepts.

Try It! *Perform the Try It! activity on the next page.*

Talk About It

Discuss the Try It! activity.

- Explain to children that solid shapes are very different from flat shapes. Display the 1" Color Cube and the sphere next to circle and square Attribute Blocks. Ask children how cubes and spheres are different from the flat shapes of the square and the circle.

- Display a ball and an orange (or other sphere). **Ask:** *How many sides do the shapes have? How many corners? How are these objects alike? How are they different?*

- Display a Color Cube, a Snap Cube®, and a cube building block (or other cube). **Ask:** *How many sides do the shapes have? How many corners? How are these shapes alike? How are they different?*

Solve It

With children, reread the problem. Place enough Color Cubes and spheres in the middle of the room so that children can come up in pairs and pick out a shape like the one Rory chose. Each child should choose a shape and then explain to a partner how they know that this is the shape Rory chose.

More Ideas

For other ways to teach about cubes and spheres—

- Provide pairs of children with 1" Color Cubes, spheres (such as rubber balls), and square and circle Attribute Blocks. Have one child choose a shape and give clues about it, including a description of its attributes, while his or her partner uses the clues to figure out the mystery shape.

- Give each pair of children a Color Cube and a ball. Have children try to find objects in the classroom that resemble these shapes.

Standardized Practice

Have children try the following problem.

Color the picture that looks like a sphere blue.
Color the picture that looks like a cube red.

Objective

Identify attributes of cubes and spheres.

Skills

- Naming shapes
- Describing attributes
- Comparing

NCTM Expectations

Geometry
- Recognize, name, build, draw, compare, and sort two- and three-dimensional shapes.
- Describe attributes and parts of two- and three-dimensional shapes.

Try It! 30 minutes | Groups of 4

Here is a problem about cubes and spheres.

Rory brought a building block and a rubber ball to school to play with during recess. When it was time to go outside, Rory reached into her backpack and grabbed one of the toys. It had no sides. Which toy did Rory grab?

Introduce the problem. Then have children do the activity to solve the problem. Before starting the activity, place one 1" Color Cube or one rubber ball in each bag.

Materials

- 1" Color Cubes (1 per group)
- rubber balls, such as a tennis ball (1 per group)
- paper bags (2 per group)

1. Distribute bags with cubes in them. Have children reach into the bag and feel the shape without looking. List children's descriptions of the shape on paper. Ask children what shape they think it is and why. Encourage them to say how they know and use words that describe what a cube is like.

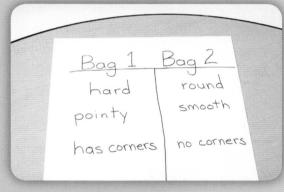

2. Distribute bags with balls in them. Have children reach into the bag and feel the shape without looking. Then list their descriptions of the shape.

3. Have children look in the bags. Allow them to remove the sphere and the cube and examine them. Tell them that the object in the first bag is a cube and the object in the second bag is a sphere.

⚠ Look Out!

Many children may have difficulty pronouncing the word *sphere.* Practice saying the word together as a class until it becomes easier. Also, watch for children who have difficulty identifying a cube or a sphere. Give the child that geometric solid to hold and touch as he or she describes the shape to you.

Geometry

Geometric Pictures and Designs

Combining shapes to form pictures and designs can help children gain a better understanding of geometric relationships. In this lesson, children will use Attribute Blocks to create pictures and abstract designs. As they become familiar with the shapes and talk about their designs, they will begin to develop spatial reasoning.

> **Try It!** *Perform the Try It! activity on the next page.*

Talk About It

Discuss the Try It! activity.

- **Ask:** *What are some shapes you see in the picture?* Make sure that children are able to identify square, rectangle, triangle, and circle.

- **Ask:** *How many squares are there in the picture? How many triangles?* Repeat for circles and rectangles. Give children time to find all the shapes.

- **Ask:** *Can you think of some other pictures you could make with these shapes? Could you make a boat? Could you make an ice cream cone?* Allow children to experiment with the shapes to help them imagine what pictures could be created.

Solve It

With children, reread the problem. Ask children to think about what shapes Ben might have used to make a picture of a house. Have them draw a house using any or all of the four shapes Ben's class used. Then have children color their houses. Discuss with children what shapes they used and how they chose the shapes.

More Ideas

For other ways to teach about identifying and using shapes—

- Have children draw pictures of things that interest them. Then have them trade pictures with a partner. The partner should pick out any Attribute Block or Pattern Block shapes that he or she can find in the picture.

- Ask children to make pictures using Attribute Blocks. Ask them to share their pictures with other members of the class. Children should name the shapes they used.

Standardized Practice

Have children try the following problem.

Color the triangle in the picture red. Then color the circle in the picture yellow.

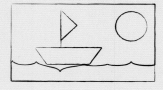

Try It! | 15 minutes | Independent

Here is a problem about geometric pictures and designs.

Mr. Jones's class is making Attribute Block pictures. The shapes they are using are squares, circles, rectangles, and triangles. Ben would like to make a picture of a house. What blocks could Ben use to make his picture?

Introduce the problem. Then have children do the activity to solve the problem.

Distribute blocks and Shape Landscapes (BLM 7) to children.

Materials
- Attribute Blocks (an assortment of same-size squares, circles, rectangles, and triangles per child)
- Shape Landscape (BLM 7; 1 per child)

1. Encourage children to explore the blocks. Review names of the block shapes with which children are familiar (circle, square, rectangle, and triangle). Ask children to look at the picture in the Shape Landscape. Ask them to describe what things they see in the picture, such as a house, a tree, and so on.

2. Ask children to look for block shapes in the picture. When they find a shape, have them identify it by name. Encourage children to describe the block shapes and the shapes in the Shape Landscape by number of sides and corners. Have children color the shapes they find.

3. Have volunteers name all of the shapes they have found and hold up the corresponding blocks.

⚠ Look Out!

If children have trouble finding shapes in the picture, hold up individual blocks and have children review their attributes. For example, remind children that a square has four sides that are all the same length. Then ask them if they can find a shape in the picture that has four sides that are all the same length.

Geometry

Geometric Problems

Solving geometric problems teaches children to utilize their spatial visualization skills. In this lesson, children will learn about geometric relationships by breaking apart shapes to create new shapes. Through their hands-on discovery, they will begin to use navigational techniques as they position shapes in different ways to make them fit on top of other shapes. Hands-on exploration makes an abstract concept such as visualization more concrete.

Objective

Use visualization and geometric modeling to solve problems.

Skills

- Spatial visualization
- Geometric relationships
- Problem solving

NCTM Expectations

Geometry
- Recognize and apply slides, flips, and turns.
- Create mental images of geometric shapes using spatial memory and spatial visualization.

Try It! *Perform the Try It! activity on the next page.*

Talk About It

Discuss the Try It! activity.

- **Ask:** *What shapes did you use to cover the red shape?* Invite children to draw their solutions on the board or show them with Pattern Blocks. Then have children name the shapes with which they are familiar, such as the square and triangle.

- **Ask:** *Did you have to move a shape to make it fit?* Ask children to demonstrate any of the ways they moved their shapes to make them fit.

Solve It

With the children, reread the problem. Ask children to draw a square and then draw a line through it to make two new shapes. Point out that the shapes they make depend on where they draw their lines. Invite children to draw three possible shapes Alex might have made by drawing a straight line through a square.

More Ideas

For other ways to teach about solving geometric problems—

- Have children explore other combinations of Pattern Blocks that can be used to make different shapes. For example, they can cover the hexagon with two trapezoids.

- Have children use Attribute Blocks and work with a partner to make up and solve geometric problems. For example, **say:** *I can be made with 2 squares.* **Ask:** *What shape am I?* (a rectangle)

Standardized Practice

Have children try the following problem.

Draw one line through the shape to make two triangles.

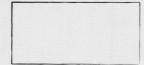

Try It! 25 minutes | Pairs

Here is a problem demonstrating geometric problem solving.

Sophia and Alex are using chalk to draw different shapes on the playground. Sophia took a piece of chalk and drew a square. Alex drew a straight line through the square to make two new shapes. What shapes could Alex have made by drawing a line through a square?

Introduce the problem. Then have children do the activity to solve the problem.

Distribute Pattern Blocks to pairs of children. For children who are not familiar with trapezoids, refer to the trapezoid children are using as "the red shape."

Materials
• Pattern Blocks (several per pair including 1 trapezoid, 1 hexagon, and an assortment of triangles, rhombuses, and squares)

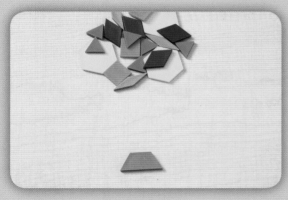

1. Direct children's attention to the red trapezoid. **Say:** *Look at the red shape. We are going to cover it with other shapes. We will cover the whole shape with no shapes hanging over the edge of it.*

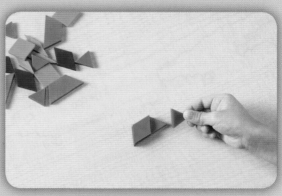

2. Have children work in pairs to arrange other blocks on top of a trapezoid. Tell children that they may need to move a shape (turn it around or flip it over) to make it fit. Demonstrate turning a block and flipping it so that children can see how this is done.

3. Once children have come up with one way to cover the trapezoid, **ask:** *Can you think of another way to cover the red shape?* Have children try to come up with a second way to cover the trapezoid with other shapes.

⚠ Look Out!

In an effort to cover the entire area of the trapezoid, some children may allow shapes to hang over the edge of the trapezoid. If this occurs, try flipping the shapes over and placing the trapezoid on top of the other shapes children are using. This will help children understand that they are using the wrong shapes, or too many shapes, to cover the trapezoid.

Geometry

Top, Middle, and Bottom

As children become familiar with location, they develop spatial reasoning. This lays a foundation for beginning navigational skills. Understanding the positioning of objects allows children to begin to create mental maps, which is a life skill. In this lesson, children will use the words *top, middle,* and *bottom* to describe the location of Snap Cubes®.

Try It! *Perform the Try It! activity on the next page.*

Talk About It

Discuss the Try It! activity.

- **Say:** *Look at the stack of Cubes on your desk.* **Ask:** *Which Cube is on top of the stack? How can you remember where the top is?*
- **Ask:** *Which Cube is in the middle? How can you remember where the middle is?*
- **Ask:** *Which Cube is on the bottom?* **Say:** *Name some ways you can remember where the bottom is.*
- Point out the difference between *top, middle,* and *bottom* and *first, second,* and *third.* Stress that *top, middle,* and *bottom* are only used to indicate vertical order, whereas *first, second,* and *third* may describe either vertical or ordinal position.

Solve It

With the children, reread the problem. Invite children to draw a bookshelf with three shelves. Ask them to use markers or crayons to draw the red block on top, the blue block in the middle, and the green block on the bottom.

More Ideas

For other ways to teach about the positions *top, middle,* and *bottom*—

- Invite children to make stacks of three different Pattern Block shapes and identify which block shapes are in the positions *top, middle,* and *bottom.*
- Have children work in pairs using the "bookshelves" they drew and Three Bear Family® Counters to further explore the concepts of top, middle, and bottom. One child places one or more Bears on the top shelf, one or more in the middle, and one or more on the bottom. The other child identifies which Bear or Bears are in each position. Children take turns arranging the Bears and naming their positions.

Standardized Practice

Have children try the following problem.

Circle the Cube that is in the middle. Then place an X on the Cube that is on the bottom.

Objective

Identify the positions *top, middle,* and *bottom.*

Skills

- Spatial reasoning
- Navigation
- Learning directions

NCTM Expectations

Geometry
- Describe, name, and interpret relative positions in space and apply ideas about relative position.

Try It! 15 minutes | Pairs

Here is a problem demonstrating *top, middle,* and *bottom.*

Ms. Diaz's class has a bookshelf with three shelves. Ms. Diaz asked Theresa to place a red block on the top shelf, a blue block on the middle shelf, and a green block on the bottom shelf. Can you draw a picture of the blocks on the bookshelf?

Introduce the problem. Then have children do the activity to solve the problem.

Pass out Snap Cubes® to children.

Materials
• Snap Cubes® (1 blue, 1 red, and 1 green per pair)

1. Direct children to look around the classroom. Point out objects that are on top of other objects. Instruct pairs of children to set the blue Cube in front of them on the desk or table.

2. Now tell children to put the red Cube on top of the blue Cube. **Say:** *The red Cube is on top. The blue Cube is on the bottom.*

3. Tell children to put a green Cube on the bottom of the stack. **Say:** *The blue Cube was on the bottom before. Now the green Cube is on the bottom. The blue Cube is in the middle.* Practice the concept of top, middle, and bottom by instructing children to build more three-Cube towers.

⚠ Look Out!

Watch for children who might automatically assume that the first color Cube mentioned is the one that goes on the top. Try mixing up the way you state the positioning by starting with the bottom Cubes some of the time. Also, be sure that students do not confuse the positions *top, middle,* and *bottom* with ordinal numbers such as *first, second,* and *third.*

Geometry

Positions in a Line

In our daily lives, we are often confronted with situations requiring directional skills. As children become familiar with location, they develop spatial reasoning. This lays a foundation for beginning navigational skills. In this lesson, children will use the words *in front, behind,* and *between* as they place 1" Color Cubes in a line.

Objective

Identify the positions *in front, behind,* and *between.*

Skills

- Spatial reasoning
- Navigation
- Identifying locations

NCTM Expectations

Geometry
- Describe, name, and interpret relative positions in space and apply ideas about relative position.

Try It! *Perform the Try It! activity on the next page.*

Talk About It

Discuss the Try It! activity.

- **Ask:** *Which color is at the front of the line? Which color is behind the cube at the front of the line?* **Say:** *This cube is behind one cube and in front of another.* **Ask:** *What do we call this place in a line?* Discuss with children what it means to be between two objects. Point out that another way to say that an object is between two other objects is to say that it is in the middle.

- **Ask:** *Which color is behind the cube in the middle?*

- **Say:** *Suppose you added a purple cube to the front of your line.* **Ask:** *What colors would be behind the purple cube?*

Solve It

With children, reread the problem. Have children solve the problem by using markers or crayons to draw the order of the teams on a piece of paper. Children may draw circles or simple stick figures in green, blue, and orange to show the correct order.

More Ideas

For other ways to teach about *in front, behind,* and *between*—

- Allow children to come up with their own color order using Three Bear Family® Counters. Children should set the Bears in a line with their faces turned the same way. Then they can turn the Bears around to see how the order changes. Have them draw pictures to show the different positions in which they place the Bears.

- To tie geometry in with number sense, have children use the directional words *in front, behind,* and *between* when describing the location of Pattern Blocks on a 0–10 Number Line (BLM 3) showing left to right directionality.

Standardized Practice

Have children try the following problem.

Which fish is between the yellow fish and the blue fish? Circle the answer.

Try It! 15 minutes | Groups of 3

Here is a problem demonstrating positions in a line.

Mr. Williams divided his class up into teams to play a game. He told the green team to stand up in front. He told the orange team to line up behind the green team. Next, he told the blue team to stand in front of the orange team. What is the order of the teams?

Introduce the problem. Then have children do the activity to solve the problem.

Distribute 1" Color Cubes to groups of three children, one cube per child. Each child in the group should get a different color.

Materials
- 1" Color Cubes (1 green, 1 orange, and 1 blue cube per group)

 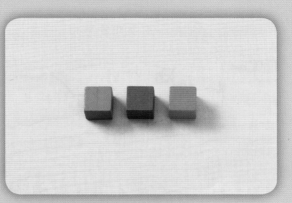

1. Each child in the group should stand up, holding his or her cube. **Say:** *The people with green cubes step away from your group and start a line. I'd like the person with the orange cube to stand behind the person with the green cube. Next, the person with the blue cube should move in front of the person with the orange cube.*

2. Once all children are in a row, have them set down their cubes in the order that matches how they are standing. Groups may compare their orders.

3. Have children mix up cubes, and then give them instructions to put cubes in a different order. Complete the activity two or three more times with other sets of directions.

⚠ Look Out!

If children have trouble following multistep directions, review the meaning of *in front, behind,* and *between* by asking children to perform only one step. Also, children might use the ordinal words *first, second,* and *third* to describe the positions in line. While these terms are correct, you will want to make sure that students are also learning the spatial terms *in front, behind,* and *between.* Additionally, make sure children understand that left-to-right order is not necessarily the same as front-to-back. The object farthest left in a line is not automatically at the front, because the location of the front of the line depends on which way objects are facing.

L E S S O N

11

Objective

Identify the positions *on,* *above,* and *below.*

Skills

- Spatial reasoning
- Navigation
- Identifying locations

NCTM Expectations

Geometry
- Describe, name, and interpret relative positions in space and apply ideas about relative position.

Geometry

Relative Locations

We use relative positioning throughout our daily lives to form mental images. When working with graphs, charts, grids, and other visual aids, words describing relative position are vital in making interpretations. In this lesson, children will use *on, above,* and *below* to determine location. They will do this by placing 1" Color Cubes on, above, and below their chairs.

Try It! Perform the Try It! activity on the next page.

Talk About It

Discuss the Try It! activity.

- **Ask:** *Which cube is below the red cube? How can you remember where* below *is?* List ideas that children come up with.

- **Ask:** *Which cube is above the yellow cube?* Make sure children understand that when something is *above* an object, it is in a place over the object. Have them come up with some ways to remember where *above* is.

- Discuss the fact that all three cubes are *on* a surface. Make sure that children see that the green cube is on the floor, the yellow cube is on the chair, and the red cube is on the desk.

Solve It

With children, reread the problem. Pass out a piece of paper to each child. As you read the problem again, have children use markers or crayons to draw how Melissa put the objects away. They can draw the table and the objects, or use yellow, red, and green circles to represent the objects and their relative positions.

More Ideas

For other ways to teach about *on, above,* and *below*—

- Have children practice using the words *on, above,* and *below* by placing Backyard Bugs™ on, above, or below a table or desk and then describing their locations. For example, "The grasshopper is above the spider."

- Have children use Attribute Blocks to practice *on, above,* and *below.* Tell them to put a red shape with three sides below their chair. Then have children put a blue shape with four sides on their chair. Continue with other shapes.

Standardized Practice

Have children try the following problem.

Circle the toy that is on the table.
Put an X on the toy below the table.

Try It! 10 minutes | Independent

Here is a problem demonstrating relative locations.

Mrs. Lane asked Melissa to put away a few of her things. She told Melissa to put her green boots below the table. She said to put her yellow book on the table. Then she said to put the red picture she made on the wall above the table. Where did Melissa put these things?

Introduce the problem. Then have children do the activity to solve the problem.

Pass out one red, one yellow, and one green 1" Color Cube to each child. **Say:** *Today we are going to use these cubes to learn words that tell where things are.*

Materials
• 1" Color Cubes (1 red, 1 yellow, and 1 green cube per child)

1. Have children stand up and hold their three cubes. Have children put their yellow cube on their chair. **Say:** *Point to the cube on the chair.* Make sure children point to the yellow cube.

2. Have children put the red cube on their desk. **Say:** *Point to the cube that is above the yellow cube.* Make sure children point to the red cube.

3. Have children put the green cube on the floor under the chair. **Say:** *Point to the cube that is below the yellow cube.* Make sure children point to the green cube.

⚠ Look Out!

Some children may get confused using the term *on* when describing location and think that if an object is next to something, it is on it. Emphasize the difference between the meanings of *on* and *next to.* Make clear to children that just because an object is close to something, it is not necessarily on it. Remind children that when using the words *on, above,* and *below,* we are describing the location of things that go up and down.

Objective

Identify the positions *inside* and *outside*.

Skills

- Describing relative positions
- Classifying locations
- Spatial reasoning

NCTM Expectations

Geometry
- Describe, name, and interpret relative positions in space and apply ideas about relative position.

Geometry

Inside and Outside

The position of any object can be described as inside or outside a given location. An object is inside a location if it is within the boundaries of the location. An object is outside a location if it is not within the boundaries of the location. Identifying the position of an object in three-dimensional space is one of the most basic descriptive steps in geometric thinking. This skill sets the stage for identifying locations such as over, under, and on. Later, this skill will help children understand measurements such as length and area.

Try It! *Perform the Try It! activity on the next page.*

Talk About It

Discuss the Try It! activity.

- **Ask:** *How are* inside *and* outside *different?*
- **Ask:** *Where is inside the circle? Where is outside the circle?*
- **Ask:** *Which shapes did you put inside the circle? Which shapes did you put outside the circle?* Encourage children to use the names of the shapes.
- If a child places a Pattern Block on the circle, point out that part of the block is inside, and part of it is outside. Also, remind students that they can use the word *on* to describe where the block is in relation to the circle.

Solve It

With children, reread the problem. Ask children to draw a circle to show the basket from the problem. Then have them draw where the ball could have landed in order for Kevin to score 1 point.

More Ideas

For other ways to teach about *inside* and *outside*—

- Have children draw shapes on sheets of paper and place Snap Cubes® inside or outside of the shape.
- Have children describe the location of Three Bear Family® Counters that are inside and outside a cup.
- Have pairs of children place Attribute Blocks inside and outside Sorting Circles based on their attributes. For example, have pairs put shapes with four corners outside the Sorting Circle and shapes with three corners inside it.

Standardized Practice

Have children try the following problem.

Draw a square inside the circle. Then draw a triangle outside the circle.

Try It! 30 minutes | Pairs

Here is a problem demonstrating the positions inside and outside.

At recess, Mrs. Miller introduced the children to a new game called Ball Toss. If a ball lands inside the basket, you score 1 point. If a ball lands outside the basket, you score 0 points. When Kevin threw the ball, he scored 1 point. Where did the ball land?

Introduce the problem. Then have children do the activity to solve the problem.

Distribute Pattern Blocks and Sorting Circles to pairs. Tell children that they will be learning about the words *inside* and *outside*.

Materials
- Pattern Blocks (several per pair)
- Sorting Circles (1 per pair)

1. Direct children to look around the classroom and notice things that are inside or outside of other things. You may want to hold up a container of blocks and tell children that the blocks are inside the container. Next, take out a block and tell children that this block is outside the container.

2. Have pairs place a Sorting Circle in front of them. Tell children that objects can also be inside or outside of a flat circle. Demonstrate by placing a block triangle inside a Sorting Circle. **Say:** *The triangle is inside the circle.* Demonstrate putting a block outside the circle as well. Then invite one child in each pair to take a block and place it on their desk either inside or outside of their circle.

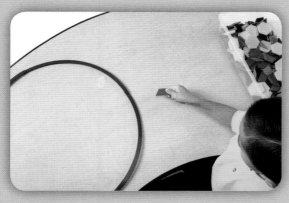

3. The other child will describe the location of the block using the word *inside* or *outside*. Invite children to take turns setting down the blocks and telling where they are placed. Encourage children to use the correct vocabulary for the shapes they are using.

⚠ Look Out!

Watch for children who confuse the words *inside* and *outside* because they sound alike. Remind children that they go outside the school for recess and come back inside the school when recess is over. Connect this idea to the activity by using counters. Have children move the counters outside the Sorting Circle for "recess." Then have children return the counters to the circle.

Geometry

77

Algebra

Algebra uses symbols to show mathematical relationships and to solve problems. The study of algebra in the elementary grades includes investigating relationships among quantities, finding ways of representing mathematical relationships, and analyzing change. Algebra builds on children's experiences with numbers and is closely linked to geometry and data analysis. In this way, the ideas taught in algebra help to unify the elementary mathematics program.

Although the formal structure of algebra may not be taught explicitly in the primary grades, children's work with algebraic concepts at this level gives them a foundation upon which they can build. For instance, working extensively with patterns helps children grasp the concepts of functions in later years. Similarly, a deep understanding of numbers and their properties developed in the elementary grades can lead to a better understanding of symbols and algebraic expressions in middle and high school.

The Grades Pre-K–2 NCTM Standards for Algebra suggest that children should:

- Understand patterns, relationships, and functions
- Represent and analyze mathematical situations and structures using algebraic symbols
- Use mathematical models to represent and understand quantitative relationships
- Analyze change in various contexts

Algebra for young children should focus on two main areas. First, children focus on making generalizations and representing mathematical ideas. Children may do so using manipulatives, drawings, or symbols. Second, children practice representing and solving problems. When children represent an addition problem with counters, for example, they are preparing for later work with modeling.

In the primary grades, the abstract ideas of algebra are introduced concretely. At an early age, children sort, classify, and order objects based on their attributes. Teachers can help children extend their patterns and make predictions about those patterns. This builds a foundation for later work with number patterns, geometric shapes, data, and change analysis. The following are activities involving manipulatives that children can use to develop skills in **Algebra.**

Algebra

Contents

Objective

Sort objects by one attribute.

Skills

- Sorting
- Classifying
- Comparing

NCTM Expectations

Algebra
- Sort, classify, and order objects by size, number, and other properties.

Geometry
- Recognize, name, build, draw, compare, and sort two- and three-dimensional shapes.

Data Analysis and Probability
- Sort and classify objects according to their attributes and organize data about the objects.

Algebra

Sort by One Attribute

As part of sorting, children must recognize and describe the attributes of an object, such as color, shape, and size. Then children must group the object with objects that share the same attribute or attributes. This requires that children identify similarities and differences in order to tell which objects belong and which do not belong. Matching and sorting objects by one attribute lays the foundation for patterning, which is a basic part of algebra.

Try It! *Perform the Try It! activity on the next page.*

Talk About It

Discuss the Try It! activity.

- **Ask:** *What is sorting?*
- **Ask:** *When you sorted the Attribute Blocks by color, how many different groups did you make? How were the blocks in each group the same?* (Repeat questions for sorting by shape and sorting by size.)
- Display the following block shapes for children: circle, square, rectangle, triangle. **Say:** *Imagine that you have a set of blocks that are circles, squares, rectangles, and triangles.* **Ask:** *If you sorted the blocks by shape, how many groups would you make?*

Solve It

With children, reread the problem. Then instruct children to draw a picture showing one of the ways that they sorted the blocks. Encourage children in each group to show the blocks sorted in different ways (by color, by shape, or by size). Then ask children to use their drawings to explain one of the ways of sorting the blocks to the other children in their group.

More Ideas

For other ways to teach about sorting objects by one attribute—

- Give each group of children an assortment of Link 'N' Learn® Links. Have children sort the Links into groups by color and make one necklace of each color.
- Give each group of children a variety of Pattern Blocks in assorted shapes. Have them sort the blocks by shape.
- Give each group of children an assortment of Three Bear Family® Counters. Then have children sort the Bear Counters into groups based on size.

Standardized Practice

Have children try the following problem.

Circle the shape that belongs with the rest.

Try It! 20 minutes | Groups of 6

Here is a problem involving sorting objects by one attribute.

Ms. Barton divided her class into groups. Then she gave each group 3 small and 3 large circles, 3 small and 3 large squares, and 3 small and 3 large triangles. Each shape and size came in yellow, red, and blue. What are three ways the children can sort the blocks?

Introduce the problem. Then have children do the activity to solve the problem. Distribute materials to each group. Make sure that the Attribute Blocks you give to each group are all the same thickness to avoid possible confusion based on this additional attribute. **Say:** *When you sort, you put things into groups with other things that are the same.*

Materials
- Attribute Blocks (3 small and 3 large of each of the following shapes in yellow, red, and blue per group: circle, square, and triangle)
- Sorting Circles (3 per group)

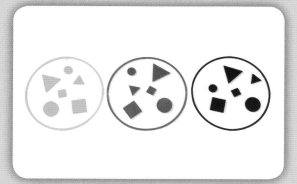

1. Say: *You will be sorting these blocks by color.* Instruct children to place the blocks in the corresponding Sorting Circles by color. Then have children check that the blocks were sorted correctly, clear the Sorting Circles, and put all of the blocks into a pile.

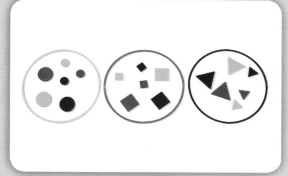

2. Say: *Now you will be sorting these blocks by shape.* Instruct children to sort the blocks by shape by putting circles in the yellow Sorting Circle, squares in the red Sorting Circle, and triangles in the blue Sorting Circle. Then have children check that the blocks were sorted correctly, clear the Sorting Circles, and put all of the blocks into a pile.

⚠ Look Out!

Watch out for children who are confused by the attributes that they are not sorting by in each step. For example, when sorting by color, children may become confused or focus on the different shapes and sizes of the blocks. Remind these children in each step that they are only sorting by one attribute.

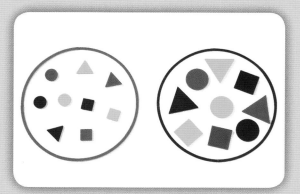

3. Say: *Now you are going to sort blocks by size.* **Ask:** *How many Sorting Circles will you need?* Guide children to the conclusion that they will need to use two Sorting Circles to sort their blocks by size (large and small). Then have children sort their blocks by size.

Algebra

Sort by Two Attributes

When sorting by two attributes, children must be able to group and regroup the objects by different attributes—color, shape, or size. Sorting objects by two attributes lays the foundation for types of classification that will be useful in recognizing and describing complex algebraic patterns.

Objective

Sort groups of objects by two attributes.

Skills

- Sorting
- Classifying
- Comparing

NCTM Expectations

Algebra
- Sort, classify, and order objects by size, number, and other properties.

Geometry
- Recognize, name, build, draw, compare, and sort two- and three-dimensional shapes.
- Describe attributes and parts of two- and three-dimensional shapes.

Data Analysis and Probability
- Sort and classify objects according to their attributes and organize data about the objects.

Try It! *Perform the Try It! activity on the next page.*

Talk About It

Discuss the Try It! activity.

- **Say:** *Look at the Attribute Blocks in your Sorting Circles. Tell what the blocks in each circle look like.* (Point to the upper-left Sorting Circle.) **Ask:** *What color are the blocks in this circle? What size are they?* (Repeat these questions as you point to the blocks in each Sorting Circle.)

- Display an assortment of blocks. **Ask:** *How could you sort this set of blocks? Could you sort them by color? By shape? By size?*

Solve It

With children, reread the problem. Have children draw four large circles on a sheet of paper. Then ask children to use red and blue crayons to draw the chairs to show how they should be sorted into different groups. Remind children that they are sorting the chairs by size as well as by color.

More Ideas

For other ways to teach about sorting by two attributes—

- Have children sort Three Bear Family® Counters by two attributes such as size and color.

- Tell children that they are going on a "Bug Hunt." First distribute piles of assorted Backyard Bugs™ around the classroom. Then divide the class into six groups and assign a different color of Bug to each group. Have children from each group collect all of the Bugs that match their color. Then have the children in each group work together to sort each color of Bug into six groups, based on the shapes of the Bugs.

Standardized Practice

Have children try the following problem.

Which group does a *belong in?*

A.   B.   C.   D.

Try It! 30 minutes | Groups of 6

Here is a problem involving sorting groups of objects by two attributes.

Ms. Lopez needs her class to help organize the chairs in the classroom. There are small chairs that are red and small chairs that are blue. There are large chairs that are red and large chairs that are blue. How can she make a group of chairs that are small and red? How can she make a group of chairs that are small and blue? How can she make a group of chairs that are large and red? How can she make a group of chairs that are large and blue?

Introduce the problem. Then have children do the activity to solve the problem. Distribute Attribute Blocks and Sorting Circles to each group.

Materials
- Attribute Blocks (2 sizes of red and blue blocks of 1 shape per group)
- Sorting Circles (4 per group)

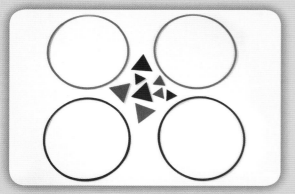

1. Have children examine their sets of blocks. Ask them to explain how the blocks in their set are alike and how they are different. Guide children to the conclusion that the blocks are all the same shape, but they are two different colors and two different sizes.

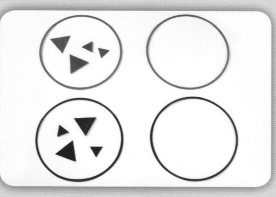

2. Have children set out their Sorting Circles in two rows of two. Have them sort the red shapes in the first circle in the top row and the blue shapes in the first circle in the bottom row. Ask children how the blocks in each circle are different now. (They are two different sizes.)

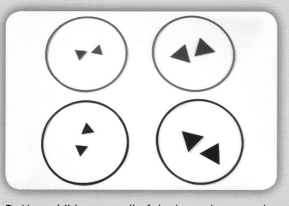

3. Have children sort all of the large shapes and move them to the second circle in each row. Then ask children to compare the blocks in each circle. (All of the shapes in each circle are exactly alike.)

⚠ Look Out!

Children may be confused by the different thicknesses of the blocks. Either remove the thick or thin blocks from the sets, or introduce thickness as another attribute and encourage children to sort their shapes one additional step by moving thin shapes to the left of each Sorting Circle and thick shapes to the right of each Sorting Circle.

Algebra

Determine the Sorting Rule

Children need to be familiar with sorting by color, shape, and size in order to determine the sorting rule for a group of objects that has already been sorted. Determining a sorting rule involves becoming aware of a pattern. This can be done by comparing groups and recognizing how the objects are similar and different. Algebraic thinking and logical reasoning are developed as children work to determine a sorting rule. These skills are at the foundation of understanding algebraic functions.

Try It! *Perform the Try It! activity on the next page.*

Objective

Determine the sorting rule for sorted groups of objects.

Skills

- Sorting
- Classifying
- Comparing

NCTM Expectations

Algebra
- Sort, classify, and order objects by size, number, and other properties.

Geometry
- Recognize, name, build, draw, compare, and sort two- and three-dimensional shapes.

Data Analysis and Probability
- Sort and classify objects according to their attributes and organize data about the objects.

Talk About It

Discuss the Try It! activity.

- **Ask:** *When I sorted the Attribute Block shapes for you, how did you know how I sorted them? What did you look for first? Did you look for different sizes? Different shapes? Different colors?*

- **Ask:** *When it was your turn, how did you sort the blocks? Did the rest of the group know how you sorted?*

- **Ask:** *What is another way you could sort the blocks?*

Solve It

With children, reread the problem. Have children draw a picture to show the books on two rows. Then have children use their pictures to explain how the books were sorted.

More Ideas

For other ways to teach determining the sorting rule—

- Have children work independently with a variety of manipulatives (one kind for each child) and sort their sets into at least two groups based on at least one attribute. Have each child keep their sorted objects at their desks. Then have children take turns going around the room, stopping at each set of sorted objects, and determining the sorting rule.

- Give each pair of children a set of objects that is sorted into two or three groups, such as two or three colors of 1" Color Cubes, two or three types of Backyard Bugs™, or two or three sizes of Three Bear Family® Counters. Then give each pair an unsorted pile of the same objects. Have children determine the sorting rule and follow the same rule to sort the new pile of objects.

Standardized Practice

Have children try the following problem.

Draw a circle around the shape on the right that matches the shapes in the Sorting Circle.

Try It! 30 minutes | Groups of 3

Here is a problem about determining a sorting rule.

Sam's teacher put the books in the reading area on two shelves. The colors and sizes are all mixed up, but Sam sees that the books on the first shelf are square and the books on the second shelf are rectangular. How did Sam's teacher sort the books?

Introduce the problem. Then have children do the activity to solve the problem. Distribute Attribute Blocks and Sorting Circles to each group.

Materials
- Attribute Blocks (an assortment of sizes, shapes, and colors for each group)
- Sorting Circles (2 per group)

1. Set up two Sorting Circles that demonstrate sorting by shape for each group of children. Encourage children to work together to find that the two groups of blocks have been sorted by shape. Have children finish this sentence: The blocks have been sorted by [shape].

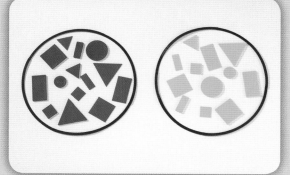

2. Repeat Step 1 with two new shapes. Then repeat to show two groups sorted by color and two groups sorted by size. Have children finish this sentence after determining each sorting rule: The blocks have been sorted by [attribute].

⚠ Look Out!

Watch out for children who incorrectly determine the sorting rule. Have these children practice sorting a group of blocks by shape, color, or size. Then try the activity again by giving children a presorted group and having them determine the rule.

3. After children have determined the sorting rules for the blocks that you have sorted, have them take turns sorting the blocks and determining the sorting rule.

Algebra

Extend Color Patterns

Identifying and extending a color pattern involves recognizing how the colors in the pattern are organized. Children must understand that patterns involve repetition in order to understand how a pattern should be extended. Recognition of patterns is one of the most important skills in the development of algebraic reasoning.

Try It! *Perform the Try It! activity on the next page.*

Talk About It

Discuss the Try It! activity.

- While discussing the activity, make sure to emphasize that a pattern is something that repeats itself. **Ask:** *What is a pattern? How do you know when you have a pattern?* **Say:** *Explain how the objects in the pattern were alike. Explain how they were different.*

- **Ask:** *What color Snap Cube® came next in the pattern?*

- Display a train of Cubes (red, blue, red, blue, red). **Ask:** *How did you know the blue Cube was missing from the end of this pattern train?* **Say:** *Now add the next two Cubes in the color pattern.* (red, blue)

Solve It

With children, reread the problem. Have children draw Mr. Matthews's construction-paper path. Make sure that they color the path to match the pattern. Then have children use their drawings to explain Mr. Matthews's pattern and tell how they knew what came next.

More Ideas

For other ways to teach about identifying and extending a color pattern—

- Give pairs of children a variety of Snap Cubes. Have each child make a color-pattern train with the Cubes. Then have children switch trains and extend their partner's train by one Cube.

- Give each group of children several Three Bear Family® Counters that are all the same size. Have one child use Bears to start a pattern. Then have each child in the group add Bears to extend the pattern as they tell a story about the Bears. For example, one yellow Bear and one red Bear went on a picnic, one yellow Bear and one red Bear went swimming, one yellow Bear and one red Bear went for a walk, and so on.

Standardized Practice

Have children try the following problem.

Find the pattern. Then color the last triangle to show the color that goes next.

Objective

Identify and extend a color pattern.

Skills

- Recognizing patterns
- Extending patterns
- Predicting

NCTM Expectations

Algebra

- Sort, classify, and order objects by size, number, and other properties.
- Recognize, describe, and extend patterns such as sequences of sounds and shapes or simple numeric patterns and translate from one representation to another.
- Analyze how both repeating and growing patterns are generated.

Try It! 20 minutes | Pairs

Here is a problem about identifying and extending a color pattern.

Mr. Matthews is making a path of colored construction paper leading from the inside of the classroom to the playground. He wants the path to make a color pattern. He has started the pattern in this order: red, blue, red, blue, red. What color should go next?

Introduce the problem. Display a simple *AB* color-pattern train of Snap Cubes®. Tell children that a pattern is a set of things that repeats in order. Explain that a color pattern is a set of colors that repeat in a specific order. Then have children do the activity to solve the problem. Distribute Cubes to each pair of children.

Materials
- Snap Cubes® (10 red Cubes and 10 blue Cubes per pair)

1. Have children work in pairs to make a pattern train of Cubes in the following order: red, blue, red, blue, red.

2. Say: *I guess that the next Cube in the pattern train is red.* Tell children to add a red Cube to the end of the train. Have them examine the train. Then, **ask:** *Was my guess correct? Does the red Cube belong at the end of the train?* Guide children to recognize that the red Cube is not placed correctly. Have children remove the red Cube from the end of the train.

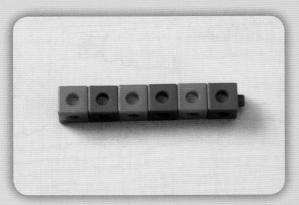

3. Say: *The red Cube was not correct.* **Ask:** *What Cube should we try next?* Have children add a blue Cube. **Ask:** *Does the blue Cube belong at the end of the train?* Guide children to recognize that the blue Cube correctly extends the pattern. Then ask children to explain the repeating pattern of the Cubes in the train (1 red and 1 blue).

⚠ Look Out!

Some children may have trouble determining the pattern and understanding how it was extended, even after adding the blue Cube to its correct place at the end of the train. Have children start at the beginning of the train (red, blue, red, blue, red, blue) and break the train apart by color as they explain the number and color of the Cubes they are removing. Use the cadence of your voice to help establish the rhythm of the pattern. For example, **say:** *red, blue,* (pause), *red, blue,* and so on.

Algebra

Extend Shape Patterns

In order to identify and extend a shape pattern, children must be able to differentiate between shapes. Once the pattern is identified, children need to use the pattern to make a prediction about what comes next. Implicit in making a prediction is the understanding that patterns involve repetition. Both recognition of patterns and making predictions are skills that children will use in algebraic thinking when working with functions and in data analysis when predicting a trend in data.

Try It! *Perform the Try It! activity on the next page.*

Talk About It

Discuss the Try It! activity.

- **Ask:** *What is a shape pattern?*
- **Ask:** *What shapes were in the first pattern? What shapes did you use to continue the pattern?*
- **Ask:** *What shapes were in the second pattern? What shapes did you use to continue the pattern?*

Solve It

With children, reread the problem. Ask children to make a drawing of Javier's necklace. Tell children that the necklace should be made of 6 beads. Encourage children to then make up and draw their own necklace patterns below Javier's. Ask them to explain how the two necklace patterns are alike and how they are different.

More Ideas

For other ways to teach about identifying and extending a pattern with shapes—

- Have small groups of children work together using two types of Pattern Blocks, such as triangles and squares, to create shape patterns. Then have children switch places with another group, and have each group work to identify and extend the other group's shape pattern.

- Give each pair of children 8 Backyard Bugs™ (4 beetles and 4 caterpillars in the same color per pair). Tell children that they need to organize the Bugs in a pattern to march in a parade. Have children start the pattern with 1 beetle, 1 caterpillar, 1 beetle, 1 caterpillar, and 1 beetle. Then have children add the next Bug Counter to the marching pattern.

Standardized Practice

Have children try the following problem.

Draw the missing shape to complete the pattern.

Objective

Identify and extend a shape pattern.

Skills

- Recognizing patterns
- Extending patterns
- Making predictions

NCTM Expectations

Algebra

- Sort, classify, and order objects by size, number, and other properties.
- Recognize, describe, and extend patterns such as sequences of sounds and shapes or simple numeric patterns and translate from one representation to another.
- Analyze how both repeating and growing patterns are generated.

Try It!   20 minutes | Groups of 4

Here is a problem about identifying and extending a shape pattern.

As an art project in Javier's class, each child will make a necklace out of beads. Javier starts his pattern with a triangle bead, a square bead, a triangle bead, a square bead, and a triangle bead. What bead comes next in the necklace pattern?

Introduce the problem. Then have children do the activity to solve the problem. Distribute Attribute Blocks to each group of children.

Materials
• Attribute Blocks

1. Have children put their blocks in the following order: triangle, square, triangle, square. Explain to children that this is a shape pattern. Then **ask:** *What shape do you think should come next?*

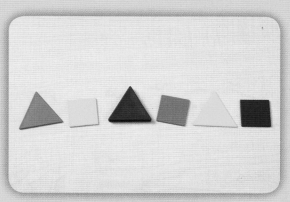

2. Have children try their guesses by placing that block next to the square at the end of the pattern. Instruct children to examine the rest of the pattern, as well as the shape they just added, to determine whether or not the block they just added was correct. If it was correct, ask children to add the next block. If it was not correct, have children remove the square block, replace it with the triangle, and check the pattern again.

⚠ Look Out!

If children have trouble identifying and extending the shape pattern, give them an identical set of blocks and have them repeat the pattern below the one that was already made as they describe the shape and the place of the shape aloud. For example, "A triangle is first, a square is second," and so on.

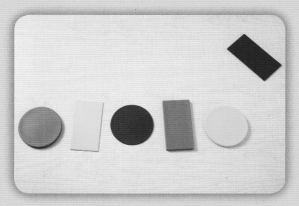

3. After all groups have correctly extended the first shape pattern, have children put blocks together to show another pattern: circle, rectangle, circle, rectangle. Have children describe the order of the shapes, add a circle to the end of the pattern, and work together to determine the pattern and add the next shape.

Algebra

Extend Growing Patterns

In order to identify and extend a growing pattern, children must understand that the pattern is continuing to grow. This involves making a determination about which elements of the pattern remain the same and which elements of the pattern change as the pattern continues to grow.

Try It! *Perform the Try It! activity on the next page.*

Talk About It

Discuss the Try It! activity.

■ **Ask:** *What is a pattern? What is a growing pattern?*

■ Point to the growing pattern of houses. **Ask:** *What Pattern Blocks in the growing pattern changed? How did they change each time?*

Solve It

With children, reread the problem. Have children draw the growing pattern to show the houses. Remind children to make sure to draw all of the houses described in the problem and the house that was made by Marco. Ask children to explain the growing pattern. Then have them tell how they know the number and kind of shapes that were in the house Marco made.

More Ideas

For other ways to teach about identifying and extending a growing pattern—

■ Have pairs of children use 1" Color Cubes to build a growing pattern "up" to look like a staircase by stacking cubes on top of one another. Have them start this pattern: purple; purple, red; purple, red, red. Then have children use their cubes to build the fourth part of the pattern. Encourage children to also show the pattern in a straight line. Then have children use cubes to make their own growing patterns in different formats. Have partners identify and extend each other's patterns in the same format.

■ Have groups of three children use Three Bear Family® Counters to make and extend growing patterns. For example, the first child starts the first row of the pattern with one small red Bear Counter; the second child makes the second row with one small red Bear Counter and one medium yellow Bear Counter; the third child repeats the second row and adds a Counter to extend the pattern.

Standardized Practice

Have children try the following problem.

Color the square to show how the pattern grows.

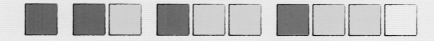

Objective

Identify and extend a growing pattern.

Skills

• Recognizing patterns
• Extending patterns
• Comparing

NCTM Expectations

Algebra
• Sort, classify, and order objects by size, number, and other properties.
• Recognize, describe, and extend patterns such as sequences of sounds and shapes or simple numeric patterns and translate from one representation to another.
• Analyze how both repeating and growing patterns are generated.

Try It! 30 minutes | Pairs

Here is a problem about identifying and extending a growing pattern.

Anissa's class is making a growing pattern of block houses. Tim is first. He starts the pattern by building one block house with one square and one triangle. Anissa goes second and builds a house with two squares and two triangles. Kim goes third and builds a house with three squares and three triangles. Marco is fourth. How many squares and triangles should Marco use to build his house?

Introduce the problem. Then have children do the activity to solve the problem. Distribute Pattern Blocks to each pair of children.

Materials
• Pattern Blocks (10 orange squares and 10 green triangles per pair)

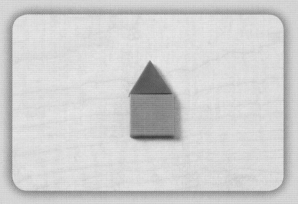

1. Display a house made of one square and one triangle block. Have children use their blocks to make the same house. **Say:** *This is a block house. We are going to make a pattern of block houses.*

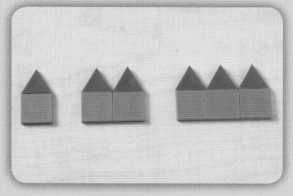

2. Add a house made of two squares and two triangles followed by a house made of three squares and three triangles. Have children make the same house pattern. Explain that in this pattern, the houses are getting bigger. **Say:** *This is a growing pattern.*

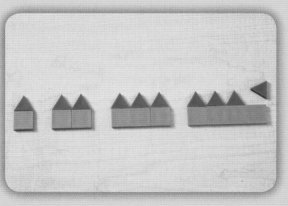

3. Have children identify each part of the pattern, and ask them to think about the fourth house. Guide children to the conclusion that the fourth house should be made of four squares and four triangles. Then have them make the fourth house.

⚠ Look Out!

If children have trouble understanding how the pattern is growing, have them build the first and second houses in the pattern, then stop and compare the houses. Then have them add the third house, compare the first to the second, compare the second to the third, and discuss what is different or what changes each time.

LESSON 7

Objective

Translate patterns from one form to another.

Skills

- Creating patterns
- Recognizing patterns
- Translating patterns

NCTM Expectations

Algebra
- Recognize, describe, and extend patterns such as sequences of sounds and shapes or simple numeric patterns and translate from one representation to another.
- Analyze how both repeating and growing patterns are generated.

Algebra

Translate Patterns

Much of the world around us consists of patterns. Our calendar and base-ten number system are only a few examples of the patterns children, as well as adults, work with every day. Because of this, it is imperative that children learn to recognize and work with patterns from an early age. Being able to create, copy, repeat, and translate a simple pattern is the beginning step in their mastery of this lifelong skill.

Try It! *Perform the Try It! activity on the next page.*

Talk About It

- Display the two Color Tile patterns from Steps 1 and 2 of the Try It! activity. **Ask:** *How are these two patterns the same?*
- Add the green and blue Pattern Block pattern from Step 2 of the Try It! activity to the pattern display. **Ask:** *How is this pattern the same as the two tile patterns? Does it follow the same pattern rule? What is the pattern rule?*
- **Ask:** *What pattern rule did you use to make your pattern? What shapes and colors did your partner use to show the same rule?*

Solve It

With children, reread the problem. Then have children draw a Color Tile pattern and draw a Pattern Block pattern that follows the same rule. Encourage children to explain how the patterns they drew are the same.

More Ideas

For other ways to teach about translating patterns—

- Have five volunteers stand in a given pattern, such as girl, boy, girl, boy, girl, in front of the classroom. Instruct children to represent the pattern using Attribute Blocks. Then ask children to use Color Tiles to show what the pattern would look like if it included ten children.
- Demonstrate an *AB* sound pattern for children, such as snap, clap, snap, clap, and so on. Have children snap and clap to show the pattern. Then challenge children to represent the sound pattern with Color Tiles.

Standardized Practice

Have children try the following problem.

Circle the pattern below that matches this pattern of squares.

Try It! 15 minutes | Pairs

Here is a problem about translating patterns from one form to another.

Marina's class played a pattern game. One person made a pattern with Color Tiles. Then the next person followed the same pattern rule to make a Pattern Block pattern. How did the children follow the same rule to make patterns out of tiles and blocks?

Introduce the problem. Then have children do the activity to solve the problem. Distribute an assortment of tiles and blocks to each pair of children.

Materials
- Color Tiles (20 assorted colors per pair)
- Pattern Blocks (20 assorted shapes and colors per pair)

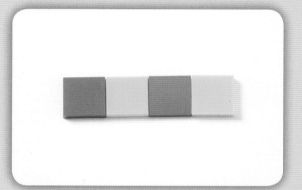

1. Have children make a red, yellow, red, yellow, red, yellow pattern using tiles. Ask children to describe the pattern by identifying both the color and number of each tile (one red tile, one yellow tile, and so on). Then ask children to describe the pattern without the color words (one of one kind followed by one of another kind or an *AB* pattern).

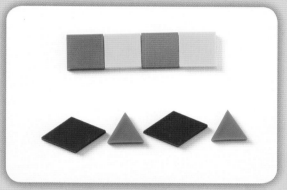

2. Ask children to use green and blue tiles to make a pattern that follows the same rule. Then instruct children to build the same *AB* pattern using green blocks in place of the green tiles and blue blocks in place of the blue tiles.

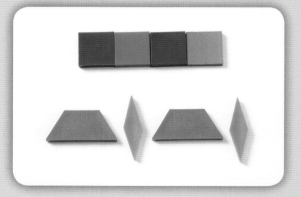

3. Have children work together to make and translate *AB* patterns using tiles and blocks. Then ask children to describe their patterns.

⚠ Look Out!

Children may have a difficult time thinking of and creating different patterns other than the *AB* color pattern they created with the class. Remind children that patterns can include a variety of colors and may have more than one of the same color in a row. Show children examples of several tile patterns for reference: *AB; AAB; AAAB; ABB; ABBB;* and so on. Encourage children to be creative as they make and translate each other's patterns.

Algebra

Three-Object Patterns

Much of our world is comprised of patterns. Children work with patterns every day as they count, listen to music, sing songs, and recite familiar rhymes. Children learn to recognize patterns in our base-ten number system as they build mathematical understanding. It is important that children learn to recognize the patterns around them, and then be able to repeat and extend these patterns.

Try It! *Perform the Try It! activity on the next page.*

Objective

Make and extend a three-object pattern and identify patterning rules.

Skills

- Identifying patterns
- Extending patterns
- Creating patterns

NCTM Expectations

Algebra
- Recognize, describe, and extend patterns such as sequences of sounds and shapes or simple numeric patterns and translate from one representation to another.
- Analyze how both repeating and growing patterns are generated.

Talk About It

Discuss the Try It! activity.

- **Ask:** *How many different kinds of Pattern Blocks did we use in our pattern?*
- **Say:** *Tell me how you knew what to add to the pattern.*
- **Ask:** *Was the pattern rule orange block, green block, blue block or green block, orange block, blue block?*

Solve It

With children, reread the problem. Give each child a piece of paper and crayons. Tell children to imagine that the paper is the art table. Then have children draw the supplies that Juan's teacher put on the table. Guide children to draw the supplies in order to repeat the pattern three times (*ABC, ABC, ABC*).

More Ideas

For other ways to teach about extending and identifying three-object patterns—

- Have each pair of children create a pattern with three different types of manipulatives such as Snap Cubes®, Color Tiles, and Pattern Blocks and repeat it one time. Then have the pairs rotate around the room so that they are at another pair's pattern. Have children identify the pattern and add objects to extend each pair's pattern with another repetition.

- Challenge children to go on a pattern scavenger hunt. Have them explore the classroom to find any patterns or the beginnings of patterns that are made up of three different objects. Then have children use three different manipulatives to copy and extend the pattern as they explain the pattern rule.

Standardized Practice

Have children try the following problem.

Circle the set of objects that comes next in the pattern.

A.

B.

Try It! 15 minutes | Pairs

Here is a problem that demonstrates making and extending a three-object pattern and identifying patterning rules.

Juan's teacher asks him to help hand out art supplies for his classmates. His teacher puts a paintbrush, a piece of paper, and a cup of paint on the table for the first child. She then adds a paintbrush, a piece of paper, and a cup of paint for the second child. She tells Juan to repeat the pattern to line up the supplies for each child. What should go next on the table?

Introduce the problem. Then have children do the activity to solve the problem. Distribute an assortment of Pattern Blocks to each pair of children.

Materials
- Pattern Blocks (4 green triangles, 4 orange squares, and 4 blue parallelograms and other assorted block shapes per pair)

1. Have children start the following pattern with their blocks: green, orange, blue, green, orange, blue. Encourage children to describe the blocks in order. Explain that the pattern starts over and repeats after the third block.

2. Have children suggest the next block. Then have them add the suggested block and evaluate the pattern to see whether the block was correct. Continue this process until the *ABC* pattern has been correctly repeated. Then have children explain the patterning rule.

3. After children have correctly extended the original pattern, have partners work together to make and extend their own three-object (*ABC*) patterns.

⚠ Look Out!

Children may try to extend the pattern by adding a unique item to the end. When showing a repeating *ABC* pattern to children, explain that this pattern is complete, and the same objects should be added to the end in the same order to show the same pattern again (*ABC-ABC-ABC*).

Algebra

Arranging Sets of Objects

In this lesson, children will learn that sets of objects with the same number of items can be arranged in different ways. A set of 8 items, for example, can be arranged in rows of 3 and 5 or 2 and 6. Children will also begin to understand simple addition and number families.

Try It! *Perform the Try It! activity on the next page.*

Talk About It

Discuss the Try It! activity.

■ **Ask:** *Did you find two different ways to arrange your Three Bear Family®️ Counters?* Have children look at one of the ten-frame arrangements. **Ask:** *How many Counters do you have in the first row? In the second row?* Have children look at the second ten-frame arrangement and answer the same questions.

■ Have children compare the two arrangements. **Say:** *You should have the same number of Counters in both ten frames.*

■ Make sure children understand that no matter how the 6 Bears are arranged, there are still the same number of Counters. **Say:** *A number can be arranged in many ways.* (For example, 5 and 1, 3 and 3, and 4 and 2.)

Solve It

With children, reread the problem. On the Ten-Frame Worksheet (BLM 8), have children draw 3 chairs on one side and 3 chairs on the other side of the first ten frame and draw 4 chairs on one side and 2 chairs on the other side of the second ten frame. Have them count the number of chairs on each ten frame. Make sure that they understand that both ten frames have 6 colored chairs and show a set of 6 items.

More Ideas

For other ways to teach about arranging sets of objects—

■ Have groups of children use 1" Color Cubes to make four-cube towers. Then have children rearrange the cubes so that they are in a line or in a square. Point out that the different arrangements show the same number.

■ Give each group a train of 9 green Snap Cubes®️ and an assortment of green and yellow Cubes. Have children make a train of green and yellow Cubes that also shows the number 9. Then have them line up the trains to reinforce the idea that the different arrangements are equal sets.

Standardized Practice

Have children try the following problem.

Circle the groups that show the same number.

Try It! 15 minutes | Pairs

Here is a problem demonstrating how to arrange sets of objects.

One of the tables in Anthony's classroom has 3 chairs on one side and 3 chairs on the other side. Another table has 2 chairs on one side and 4 on the other. How can Anthony figure out whether each table has the same number of chairs?

Introduce the problem. Then have children do the activity to solve the problem.

Arrange children in pairs, distribute Three Bear Family® Counters, and give each child a Ten-Frame Worksheet (BLM 8).

Materials
• Three Bear Family® Counters (6 per child)
• Ten-Frame Worksheet (BLM 8; 1 per child)

1. Have children count out 6 Bears. Tell children that they will be showing the number 6 on their worksheets.

2. Invite children to place the Counters on their worksheets. Each child should try to arrange the Counters in a different way than their partner.

3. Ask children to write the number of Bears (6) at the top of their worksheets. Have children count the Bears to make sure everyone has the same number. Discuss the difference in how partners placed the Bears (4 and 2, 3 and 3, or 5 and 1), but conclude that each still shows 6 Bears. Repeat the activity with other numbers as time allows.

⚠ Look Out!

Children may believe that counters arranged in a different manner represent different numbers. Be sure to count the total in each set to show that the sets contain the same number of items, despite their difference in appearance. Have children act out the concept by asking a group of 6 children to sit at a table. With the class, count the children. Then rearrange the group of 6 and count again to compare.

Measurement

Measurement is the assignment of a value to an attribute of an object, such as length, area, or mass. In the elementary grades, children first learn to determine what a measurable attribute is. Next, they must become familiar with the units and processes of measuring. Finally, children must become proficient in using the tools, techniques, and formulas used in measurement.

Measurement is a practical and pervasive part of everyday life. In the school setting, measurement connects several areas of mathematics—number operations, geometry, and statistics—as well as connecting to other subject areas such as social studies, science, art, and physical education. The study of measurement lends itself to the use of manipulatives and concrete objects. It is nearly impossible for a child to gain a full understanding of measurement without handling materials, making physical comparisons, and using measuring tools.

The Grades Pre-K–2 NCTM Standards for Measurement suggest that children should:

- Understand measurable attributes of objects and the units, systems, and processes of measurement
- Apply appropriate techniques, tools, and formulas to determine measurements

In the primary grades, the first step to understanding measurement is to recognize measurable attributes. The focus should be on length, with young children physically comparing and ordering objects. Weight, time, area, and volume should also be explored at this level. The second step to developing an understanding of measurement is learning how to choose appropriate units. In the early years of primary education, children should explore measurement with nonstandard units. This helps them develop an understanding of the necessity for standard units. The following are activities involving manipulatives that children can use to develop skills in **Measurement.**

Measurement

Contents

Measurement

Nonstandard Measurement of Height

Children may be familiar with height. They may have been measuring their growth on a wall at home, comparing their height to that of a family member, or waiting to be tall enough for a certain activity. In this lesson, children will learn to measure height in nonstandard units, which lays a foundation for later being able to use more abstract standard units of measure, such as inches and feet.

Try It! *Perform the Try It! activity on the next page.*

Talk About It

Discuss the Try It! activity.

- **Ask:** *What are some things that people measure for height?* Help children think of objects, such as buildings, trees, and so on.

- **Say:** *Explain how you find out how tall something is by using Link 'N' Learn® Links.*

Solve It

With children, reread the problem. Have children draw a picture showing how Jordan could measure the height of the jar with Links.

More Ideas

For other ways to teach about nonstandard measurements of height—

- Have children work in pairs. Each child will trace his or her partner on a large piece of paper. Then children will attach their outlines to the wall and measure the height using Link 'N' Learn Links.

- Have children work in pairs to play a guessing game. Children choose a classroom object and each child guesses the object's height in Link 'N' Learn Links (or Snap Cubes®). Then children measure the object's height with Links (or Cubes) to see whose guess was closest.

Standardized Practice

Have children try the following problem.

How many Links tall is the milk carton?

Try It! 10 minutes | Pairs

Here is a problem demonstrating how to use nonstandard units to measure height.

In Jordan's classroom, there is a jar where children put paintbrushes when they are not using them. Jordan's teacher asks the class to find out how tall the jar is. She says that they will measure the jar using Link 'N' Learn® Links. How can Jordan find out the height of the jar?

Introduce the problem. Tell children that they will use Links to find the height of classroom objects. Explain that height tells how tall something is. Demonstrate for children how to make a chain of Links that is the height of a classroom object, such as the leg of a chair. Then have children do the activity to solve the problem. Distribute Links to children.

> **Materials**
> • Link 'N' Learn® Links (50 per pair)

1. Ask children to choose an object in the classroom and estimate its height. Encourage them to make a chain that is the same height as the object.

2. Now have children check their chains against the object they are measuring. For example, if children choose a table to measure, **say:** *Hold your chain beside the table to see if they are the same height.* Children may have to add or take away Links to make their chains the same height as the objects they are measuring.

3. Have children make sure their chains match the height of the object. Then ask children to share their final measurements with the class.

⚠ Look Out!

Some children may choose objects to measure whose height cannot be expressed with an even number of Links. If children are confused by this, tell them that some items may be "almost" or "close to" a certain number of Links.

Measurement

Sorting by Height

It is important for children to learn the correct vocabulary for comparing the heights of objects. While they may be familiar with words such as *tall* and *short,* they may need explanations and practice using comparative words such as *tallest* and *shortest.* Use several real-life examples to reinforce these terms.

Perform the Try It! activity on the next page.

Objective

Sort objects by height.

Skills

- Vocabulary
- Measurement
- Making comparisons

NCTM Expectations

Measurement
- Recognize the attributes of length, volume, weight, area, and time.
- Compare and order objects according to these attributes.
- Measure with multiple copies of units of the same size, such as paper clips laid end to end.

Talk About It

Discuss the Try It! activity.

■ **Say:** *Name something in the classroom. Now find something taller.* **Ask:** *What is the tallest object in our classroom?* Make sure children understand the difference between tallest and highest. For example, a book on top of a bookshelf may be higher than other objects, but that does not mean it is taller than the other objects.

■ **Say:** *In the activity we just did, we made three towers. One was the shortest, one was the tallest, and one was in the middle. We can describe other things with these words.* Give children an example. **Say:** *I saw a giraffe, an elephant, and a monkey at the zoo.* **Ask:** *Which do you think was the shortest? The tallest?*

■ **Ask:** *If we are looking at several items, how can we decide which is the tallest? How can we tell which is the shortest? How could we be sure?* (measure or compare)

Solve It

With children, reread the problem. Instruct children to draw a picture of three books in the order that Ashley put them on the shelf (tallest to shortest).

More Ideas

For other ways to teach about sorting by height—

■ Have each child draw a picture of a tree. Then have each child make a chain of Link 'N' Learn® Links that shows the height of his or her tree. Have groups of three children lay their chains beside each other and compare the heights.

■ Have children work in groups of five. Give one child in each group one Snap Cube®, another child two Cubes, another three, and so on. Each child should connect the Cubes he or she has. Then children should work as a group to order the towers from shortest to tallest.

Standardized Practice

Have children try the following problem.

Use crayons to color the tallest house red.
Then color the shortest house blue.

Try It!   10 minutes | Pairs

Here is a problem demonstrating how to sort by height.

Ashley is helping her teacher put books on the shelf. The teacher told her to arrange three books from tallest to shortest. How can Ashley figure out where to place each of the books?

Introduce the problem. Then have children do the activity to solve the problem.

Show three Snap Cube® towers to the children. Ask which is the tallest, which is the shortest, and which is in the middle. Have a volunteer arrange the towers in order from tallest to shortest. Ask children to point to the towers and label each using the correct vocabulary. Repeat using three new towers. Assign children to work with partners. Give Cubes to each pair of children, and have them follow these steps.

Materials
- Snap Cubes® (several per pair)

1. Ask children to make three towers using different numbers of Cubes.

2. Have children compare the heights of the towers. **Say:** *Tell which tower is the tallest. Tell which is the shortest. Tell which is in the middle.*

3. Have children order the towers from tallest to shortest. Then ask them to compare the heights of the tallest and shortest towers. Instruct children to remove Cubes from the taller tower until it matches the shorter tower and count the removed Cubes to find the difference in height between the two towers.

⚠ Look Out!

Children may confuse the terms *tallest* and *taller* and *shortest* and *shorter*. Point out that while the middle tower is *shorter* than the tallest tower, it is not the *shortest*. Emphasize the endings of the comparison words. Connect them to other comparison words such as *faster, fastest,* or *bigger, biggest.* In addition, watch for children who confuse how tall something is with how high in the air it is. For example, they may think that because a flag is high in the air, it is taller than the objects around it.

Measurement

Sorting by Length

Measuring brings together mathematical disciplines such as geometry and number sense. Comparison of objects helps build a foundation in measurement concepts. In this lesson, children will begin using *shortest* and *longest* to describe objects while sorting them by length.

Try It! *Perform the Try It! activity on the next page.*

Objective

Sort objects by length; use the terms *shortest* and *longest*.

Skills

- Spatial visualization
- Measuring
- Comparing measurements

NCTM Expectations

Measurement
- Recognize the attributes of length, volume, weight, area, and time.
- Compare and order objects according to these attributes.
- Understand how to measure using nonstandard and standard units.
- Measure with multiple copies of units of the same size, such as paper clips laid end to end.

Talk About It

Discuss the Try It! activity.

- Emphasize the importance of left-to-right order. Make sure children understand that in the activity they just did, they always started from the left side regardless of the order in which they placed the trains.

- **Say:** *First we put the trains in order from shortest to longest.* **Ask:** *What happened to the middle train when we changed the order to longest to shortest?*

- **Ask:** *How can you be sure which train is the shortest? The longest?* (Look for children counting the number of Snap Cubes® or comparing by sight.)

- **Say:** *Let's make a new train that is eight Cubes long.* **Ask:** *Where would we put this train if we wanted to keep our trains in order from shortest to longest?*

Solve It

With children, reread the problem. Have children draw a picture that shows what Alison drew.

More Ideas

For other ways to teach about sorting objects by length—

- Give children more Snap Cubes to make trains of different sizes. Have them work with partners to sort the trains by length. Help them work on sorting more trains by first asking them to make three trains, then four, then five.

- Give children Link 'N' Learn® Links to create different-length chains and sort chains by length. Emphasize that children should lay the chains flat to measure their length.

Standardized Practice

Have children try the following problem.

Circle the pencil that is the longest.

Try It! 15 minutes | Pairs

Here is a problem demonstrating how to sort objects by length.

Alison drew a picture of three worms crawling on the ground. She showed the picture to her teacher. Her teacher said that the worms were in order from shortest to longest. How can you show the order of the worms in Alison's picture?

Introduce the problem. Then have children do the activity to solve the problem.

Divide the class into pairs. Pass out three trains of Snap Cubes® to each pair. The three trains should be of different lengths.

Materials
- Snap Cubes® (3 trains of different lengths per pair)

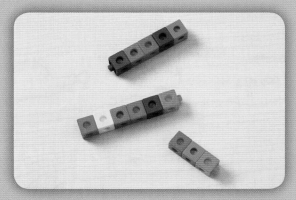

1. Instruct children to count their trains. Demonstrate if necessary.

2. Ask children to line up their trains vertically, and have them line up the left-hand sides. A straightedge can be used to help align the trains.

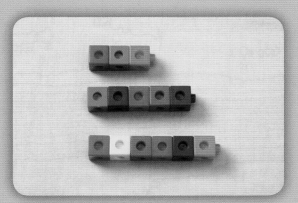

3. Now invite children to rearrange their trains from shortest to longest, with the shortest train on the top. Remind them to line up the edges of their trains correctly.

⚠ Look Out!

Watch out for the children who do not keep their trains aligned on the left ends. Model what happens when the trains are not lined up correctly to show children that the results will be skewed. Give these children a ruler or other straightedge to help them align their trains correctly. Also, make sure that children do not confuse *longest* with *tallest.* Remind children that *tallest* describes direction from the ground to the sky. Length is left to right or side to side.

Measurement

Estimating and Measuring Length

Estimating length incorporates number sense and spatial sense while creating a beginning foundation of reference points for linear measurements. In this lesson, children will estimate the length of classroom objects and then use Color Tiles to create actual measurements.

Try It! *Perform the Try It! activity on the next page.*

Objective

Estimate and measure length using nonstandard units.

Skills

- Spatial visualization
- Estimation
- Measuring

NCTM Expectations

Measurement
- Understand how to measure using nonstandard and standard units.
- Measure with multiple copies of units of the same size, such as paper clips laid end to end.

Talk About It

Discuss the Try It! activity.

- **Ask:** *How long did you think the shoe would be before you measured it? How many tiles long was the shoe? Was your guess close?*

- **Say:** *Pick another object in the room that is smaller than the length of the shoe.* **Ask:** *What do you think would be a good estimate for this object's length in tiles?* Allow children to offer their estimates for an object. Then measure the object with children to find the actual length.

- **Ask:** *If you were to measure your shoe using a chalkboard eraser, would the answer be the same? Why or why not?*

Solve It

With children, reread the problem. Have children draw a picture to show Angie's shoe being measured with tiles. Ask children to use their drawings to explain how Angie and Tim could find out who guessed correctly.

More Ideas

For other ways to teach about estimating and measuring lengths—

- Have children work in groups and use Pattern Blocks to measure a set of classroom objects. Have each group use a different block shape. Then have groups compare measurements and discuss the different measurements they get by using different blocks. Children should conclude that they need to use the same size block to get the same answers.

- Have children measure length with Snap Cubes®. Children can estimate a length and then use Cubes to measure the object to see how close their estimate is to the actual length in Cubes.

Standardized Practice

Have children try the following problem.

About how many tiles would you need to measure the length of the crayon? Circle the answer.

Try It! 25 minutes | Pairs

Here is a problem demonstrating how to estimate and measure length.

Angie wants to know how many Color Tiles long her shoe is. Tim says he thinks it is 4 tiles long. Angie thinks it is 10 tiles long. How can Angie and Tim find out how long the shoe is?

Introduce the problem. Then have children do the activity to solve the problem.

Have children work in pairs. Pass out tiles and paper to each pair.

Materials
- Color Tiles (about 50 per pair)
- paper (1 sheet per pair)

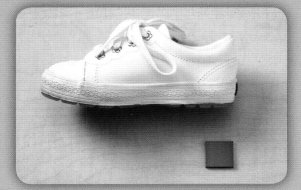

1. Have children place one tile next to one shoe. Tell them that they are going to measure the length of a shoe using the tiles.

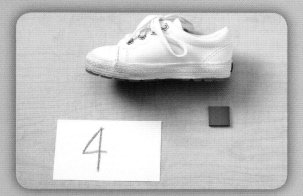

2. Ask: *How many tiles long do you think the shoe is?* Have children estimate and write down their estimates on paper.

3. Say: *Now we will measure the shoe.* Have children measure the length of the shoe with tiles. **Ask:** *How many tiles long is the shoe?* Allow children to compare the estimates they wrote down to the actual measurements.

⚠ Look Out!

Watch for children who leave gaps between tiles as they measure. Make sure children understand that they must line up the tiles in a straight line, flush with the shoe. Also discuss measuring objects that don't match evenly to whole tiles. Suggest that children round up to the nearest whole tile, or have them measure to the nearest "half-tile" if they are unable to follow the concept of rounding.

Objective

Explore the concept of perimeter.

Skills

- Spatial visualization
- Estimation
- Measuring

NCTM Expectations

Measurement
- Measure with multiple copies of units of the same size, such as paper clips laid end to end.
- Develop common referents for measures to make comparisons and estimates.

Measurement

Exploring Perimeter

Measuring and estimation are mathematical applications we use regularly in our daily lives; therefore, young children will benefit from exposure to these concepts. Measuring the perimeter of shapes ties together spatial visualization and number sense. In this lesson, children will explore the concept of perimeter by estimating the number of Color Tiles needed to measure around an index card.

Try It! *Perform the Try It! activity on the next page.*

Talk About It

Discuss the Try It! activity.

- **Ask:** *How many tiles did you think you would need to measure all the sides of the card? How many tiles did it take? How close was your guess?*
- **Ask:** *What are some other things in the classroom that you could measure around with tiles?*
- **Ask:** *If we were to measure around the card using rectangle Attribute Blocks, would we need more or fewer blocks than tiles?* Pass out some blocks so that children can come up with estimates. Then help children measure using the blocks. Help children understand that different-sized units will change the number of units needed to measure around the card.

Solve It

With children, reread the problem. Have children make a drawing to show their solution to the problem. Encourage them to show what they think Tom drew and draw the tiles on the sides of the drawing.

More Ideas

For other ways to teach about finding perimeter—

- Have children use Color Tiles to measure the perimeter of rectangle and square Attribute Blocks.
- Have pairs of children use Snap Cubes® to measure the perimeters of classroom objects, such as folders, rulers, or different-sized sheets of construction paper.

Standardized Practice

Have children try the following problem.

How many tiles would you need to measure around this shape?

Try It! 20 minutes | Pairs

Here is a problem demonstrating how to find perimeter.

Mr. Kern's class is drawing pictures. Tom wants to measure the sides of his drawing with Color Tiles. How can Tom measure the sides of his drawing with tiles?

Introduce the problem. Then have children do the activity to solve the problem.

Pass out tiles and index cards to children. They will use tiles to measure the sides of the card.

Materials
- Color Tiles (about 50 per pair)
- 3 × 5 index card (1 per pair)

1. Have children guess the number of tiles needed to measure all four sides of the card. Ask them to write their guesses on the card. Explain to children that they will be placing tiles around the edges of the card, with no space between the card and the tiles, but no tiles in the corners.

2. Instruct children to work together to place tiles around the card. Have children place the edge of a tile only against the edge of the card. Make sure they do not place tiles at the corners; the edges of the tiles must measure the edges of the card only.

3. When children have finished placing tiles around the card, have them count the number of tiles used. Ask children to write the actual number of tiles on the card and compare it to their guess.

⚠ Look Out!

Make sure that all children are lining up the tiles so that there is no space between them. Children should also place their tiles so that all the tiles are touching the edges of the card. When counting the tiles, some children may have trouble remembering where they started counting. Advise these children to put a pencil on the desk so that it points at the tile where they started.

Objective

Explore the concept of area.

Skills

- Spatial visualization
- Estimation
- Measuring

NCTM Expectations

Measurement
- Recognize the attributes of length, volume, weight, area, and time.
- Understand how to measure using nonstandard and standard units.
- Measure with multiple copies of units of the same size, such as paper clips laid end to end.

Measurement

Exploring Area

Measuring and estimation are mathematical applications used regularly in our daily lives. Young children need hands-on experience with measuring in order to create a frame of reference and build accuracy. The concept of area requires the understanding of several mathematical disciplines. Children need to be familiar with the different attributes of shapes in order to better understand area. In this lesson, children will explore the concept of area through estimating the number of Color Tiles needed to fill a square or rectangle.

Try It! *Perform the Try It! activity on the next page.*

Talk About It

Discuss the Try It! activity.

- **Ask:** *How many tiles did you guess it would take to fill the inside of Area 1?* Allow children to share their estimates.
- **Ask:** *How many tiles did it take to fill the inside of Area 1? How close was your guess?* Repeat questions for Area 2.

Solve It

With children, reread the problem. Have children draw a picture to show how Kari could solve the problem using tiles to cover her paper before cutting and gluing squares.

More Ideas

For other ways to teach about exploring the concept of area—

- Have children color in a large square or rectangle on 1-inch graph paper and find the area of the shape by covering it with Color Tiles.
- To extend the activity, have children use Color Tiles to find the area of classroom objects such as the front of a box of crayons. Help children understand that the area of these objects cannot always be covered with an exact number of tiles.

Standardized Practice

Have children try the following problem.

How many tiles can the shape hold?

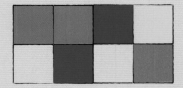

Try It!   20 minutes | Groups of 3

Here is a problem demonstrating the concept of area.

Kari's art class is cutting and gluing squares of paper like Color Tiles to fill a sheet of paper. How many squares will Kari need to cut before gluing?

Introduce the problem. Then have children do the activity to solve the problem.

Divide the class into small groups. Distribute tiles and Area Worksheets (BLM 9) to each group.

Materials
- Color Tiles (a few handfuls per group)
- Area Worksheet (BLM 9; 1 per group)

1. Tell children to look at Area 1 on their Area Worksheets. **Ask:** *How many tiles do you think will fit inside the rectangle?* Have children record their estimates.

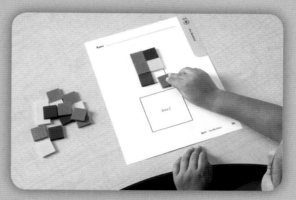

2. Instruct children to place the tiles inside Area 1 to cover the entire space. Once children are finished, have them count the number of tiles used and record the results on the Area Worksheet.

3. Repeat the activity for Area 2 on the Area Worksheet.

⚠ Look Out!

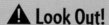

Watch for children who don't lay the tiles on the square or rectangle flat and next to each other. Some children may just pour their tiles into the middle of the shape. Try having children think of a carpet when working with area. Ask them to match the corners of the tiles to the corners of the rectangle. This helps them see that they are trying to fill a flat, confined space.

Data Analysis and Probability

The study of **Data Analysis and Probability** at the elementary-grade level has several purposes. These subject areas teach children how to ask questions, collect data, and organize and display the data in a chart or graph that answers the original questions. Children at this level also learn methods for analyzing the data to make inferences and draw conclusions. In addition to building mathematical skills, this learning allows children to become better informed citizens and intelligent consumers.

The study of data analysis connects to ideas and procedures from number, algebra, measurement, and geometry. It is also a natural way to connect mathematics instruction to children's daily lives. To develop statistical ideas, children must work directly with data. In the lower elementary grades, this may mean using census data of children in the classroom. As children progress through school, the types and uses of data become more sophisticated.

The Grades Pre-K–2 NCTM Standards for Data Analysis and Probability suggest that children should:

- Formulate questions that can be addressed with data and collect, organize, and display relevant data to answer them
- Select and use appropriate statistical methods to analyze data
- Develop and evaluate inferences and predictions that are based on data
- Understand and apply basic concepts of probability

Young children develop a beginning understanding of data through comparing, classifying, and counting activities. These understandings will progress in sophistication as children progress from pre-kindergarten through second grade. By the end of second grade, children should be able to use counts, tallies, tables, bar graphs, and line plots to display data. They should also be able to discriminate between value and frequency in the numbers their displays represent. Probability instruction at the primary level should be informal, using activities such as coin flips and dice tosses. The following are activities involving manipulatives that children can use to develop skills in **Data Analysis and Probability.**

Data Analysis and Probability

Contents

Objective

Read and interpret a pictograph.

Skills

- Counting
- Representing data
- Interpreting data

NCTM Expectations

Data Analysis and Probability
- Pose questions and gather data about themselves and their surroundings.
- Sort and classify objects according to their attributes and organize data about the objects.
- Represent data using concrete objects, pictures, and graphs.
- Describe parts of the data and the set of data as a whole to determine what the data show.

Number and Operations
- Count with understanding and recognize "how many" in sets of objects.
- Develop understanding of the relative position and magnitude of whole numbers and of ordinal and cardinal numbers and their connections.

Data Analysis and Probability

Exploring Pictographs

A bar graph compares data that do not continually change. Bar graphs make the messages in data much more visible and provide new clues about the information. They show patterns that might not be readily apparent in a text or table format. A pictograph is a special kind of bar graph that shows numerical information by using picture symbols or icons to represent data sets. In this activity, each child will create a picture that represents one birthday on a pictograph.

Try It! *Perform the Try It! activity on the next page.*

Talk About It

Discuss the Try It! activity.

- **Ask:** *How can you tell which month has the most birthdays? How can you tell which month has the fewest birthdays?* **Say:** *Show how you know.*
- **Ask:** *How many more birthdays does the month with the most have than the month with the least?*

Solve It

With children, reread the problem. Then ask each child to draw a picture of a birthday party showing the number of children that share their birth month using the pictograph as reference.

More Ideas

For other ways to teach about data collection and pictographs—

- Display one example of each Three Bear Family® Counter (Baby Bear™, Mama Bear™, Papa Bear™) and survey children about which one they like best. Represent the data on the board using tally marks. Have children make a pictograph of the data by drawing pictures to represent the different Bears.
- Survey the class to find out each child's favorite kind of pet. Give children a limited number of choices, such as dog, cat, fish, bird, or "other." Have children represent the data on a tally chart. Then have children make a pictograph of the data on the Reversible Graph It! Mat (4 × 12 Grid Side) using photos or illustrations of the different kinds of pets.

Standardized Practice

Have children try the following problem.

Jesse's class voted on which balloon color they liked best. Which color did the most children pick? Circle the row.

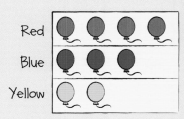

Try It! 30 minutes | Whole Class

Here is a problem about data collection and graphing.

Children in Mrs. Cole's kindergarten class are talking about their birthdays. Mrs. Cole asked the children to name their birth months. "Who was born in January? Who was born in February?" she asked. Then she said, "I want to make a graph that shows how many birthdays are in each month." Which month has the most birthdays in your class?

Introduce the problem. Then have children do the activity to solve the problem.

Cut 4" by 4" paper squares prior to the activity. Give one paper square to each child. Lay the Reversible Graph It! Mat (4 × 12 Grid Side) on the floor in an area that is easily accessible to children. Label the 12 columns with the months of the year.

Materials
- Reversible Graph It! Mat (4 × 12 Grid Side; 1 for the class)
- 4" by 4" paper squares (1 per child)
- crayons (an assortment for each child)
- clear tape (1 roll for the class)

1. Ask children to draw and color a picture of a birthday cake on their paper square.

2. Tell children that each one of their pictures shows one birthday. Help children tape their pictures in the appropriate column on the graphing mat.

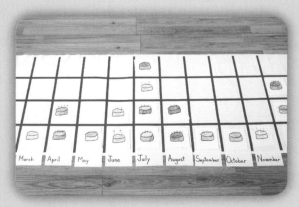

3. When children have finished, display the completed pictograph. **Ask:** *Which month has the most birthdays? Which month has the fewest birthdays?*

⚠ Look Out!

If more than four children share a particular birth month, you may need to continue a column of pictures past the edge of the graphing mat. Be sure that children understand that these pictures are still part of the pictograph.

Data Analysis and Probability

Exploring Bar Graphs

Tables, charts, and graphs make understanding and analyzing numerical data easier. A bar graph is useful for seeing at a glance which data are biggest and smallest and for introducing range, the difference between the largest and smallest values.

Try It! *Perform the Try It! activity on the next page.*

Talk About It

Discuss the Try It! activity.

■ **Ask:** *What do the towers of Snap Cubes® show?* Discuss with children the fact that the Cubes show which shirt colors are most and least common.

■ **Say:** *Look at your bar graph.* **Ask:** *Which color shirt did the most children in Miss Thorn's class wear? How do you know?*

■ **Ask:** *Do you think the most children will wear the same color tomorrow? Why or why not?*

Solve It

With children, reread the problem. Then reproduce the problem in your own class. Survey the shirt colors worn by children. Then have children work together to show the results by building a graph with Cubes and making a bar graph on paper. Have them lay the Cubes on the paper to check their graphs.

More Ideas

For other ways to teach about data collection and graphing—

■ Display an assortment of Backyard Bugs™. Ask children to choose their favorite Bug. Then, survey the class and represent the data on the board using tally marks. Have children build a graph with Snap Cubes and also draw a bar graph of the data on paper.

■ Have children work in groups using Color Tiles or Snap Cubes. Come up with data as a class. Survey children on subjects such as favorite animal, favorite season, or favorite kind of toy. Tally their responses on the chalkboard, and then help them build their bar graphs with tiles or Cubes.

Standardized Practice

Have children try the following problem.

Susan's class voted for their favorite fruit. Then they made this bar graph. Circle the fruit that got the most votes.

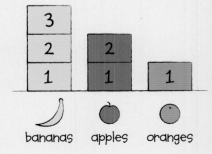

Objective

Read and interpret information in a bar graph.

Skills

- Counting
- Representing data
- Interpreting data

NCTM Expectations

Data Analysis and Probability
- Pose questions and gather data about themselves and their surroundings.
- Sort and classify objects according to their attributes and organize data about the objects.
- Represent data using concrete objects, pictures, and graphs.
- Describe parts of the data and the set of data as a whole to determine what the data show.

Number and Operations
- Count with understanding and recognize "how many" in sets of objects.
- Develop understanding of the relative position and magnitude of whole numbers and of ordinal and cardinal numbers and their connections.

Try It! 30 minutes | Pairs

Here is a problem about data collection and bar graphs.

Children in Miss Thorn's class were learning about colors. Miss Thorn said, "Look at the different colors of shirts we are wearing today. How many of each color do you count? Let's find out!" The children counted while Miss Thorn made tally marks on the board. In all, four children wore blue shirts, five wore white, two wore yellow, and seven wore red. Miss Thorn said, "Now we will make a bar graph with this information. What can we learn from a bar graph?"

Introduce the problem. Then have children do the activity to solve the problem.

To begin, discuss bar graphs and why they are useful. Then, distribute Snap Cubes® to each pair of children.

Materials
- Snap Cubes® (4 blue, 5 white, 2 yellow, and 7 red per pair)

1. Show children how to connect the Cubes in each color category to represent the data. Tell children to pretend that each Cube represents one child's shirt color.

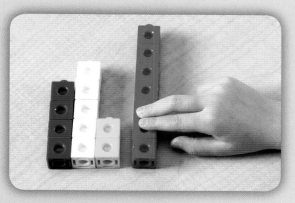

2. Direct children to arrange the Cube towers vertically to make a bar graph. Help them make the bars in the same order that the colors are listed in the problem.

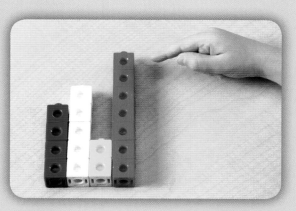

3. Ask: *Which color shirt are most children wearing? How do you know this color has the most children? Which color shirt are the fewest children wearing? How do you know?*

⚠ Look Out!

Watch for children who count all of the Cubes in each column instead of focusing on which group has more cubes. You may wish to review ways to find out which group has more without counting. In addition, children who have completed prior lessons may be inclined to order the Cubes from shortest to tallest. Asking children to put their towers in the order that the problem lists the colors will help avoid this.

Objective

Gather, record, and make a bar graph of data.

Skills

- Counting
- Recording data
- Graphing

NCTM Expectations

Data Analysis and Probability
- Pose questions and gather data about themselves and their surroundings.
- Sort and classify objects according to their attributes and organize data about the objects.
- Represent data using concrete objects, pictures, and graphs.

Number and Operations
- Count with understanding and recognize "how many" in sets of objects.
- Develop understanding of the relative position and magnitude of whole numbers and of ordinal and cardinal numbers and their connections.

Data Analysis and Probability

Graphing Data

Children should be able to gather and record data that they will later analyze. In this lesson, children will learn how to conduct a survey as a means of gathering and recording data, which they will then graph.

Try It! *Perform the Try It! activity on the next page.*

Talk About It

Discuss the Try It! activity.

- **Say:** *Look at your tally sheet. Count the X's.* **Ask:** *How many does each fruit have?*

- **Ask:** *How did you show the numbers from the tally sheet on the graph?* Make sure that children understand that they put down one Color Tile in the appropriate column for each *X* marked on the tally sheet.

- **Say:** *Look at your graph.* **Ask:** *Which fruit has the most tiles? Which has the fewest tiles?*

- **Ask:** *Which makes a longer bar, more tiles or fewer tiles?*

- Challenge children to name other things they might make graphs for. You may want to provide prompts such as the following: numbers of books children have read or numbers of people in their family.

Solve It

With children, reread the problem. Then have children transfer the manipulative graph to paper and color in the graph.

More Ideas

For other ways to teach about data collection and graphing—

- Provide each child with a handful of 1" Color Cubes. Have children sort the cubes by color, count how many cubes are in each color, and then graph the results.

- Give each pair of children an assortment of Attribute Blocks (4 different shapes). Instruct one child to sort the blocks by shape. The other child can record the data using tally marks. Children can then graph the data.

Standardized Practice

Have children try the following problem.

Anna's class made a chart to show their favorite ice cream. Which flavor do the most children like best? Circle the cone.

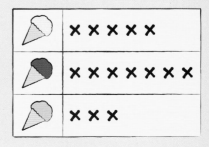

Try It! 30 minutes | Pairs

Here is a problem about data collection and graphing.

Lakewood Elementary School wants to serve fresh fruit in the cafeteria. Teachers are asking their children about their favorite fruits. How can the teachers gather the data and graph it to show the principal which fruit their class likes most?

Introduce the problem. Then have children do the activity to solve the problem.

Distribute materials to children. Then have children create a four-column tally chart by drawing a picture of each fruit (apple, banana, blueberry, pear) at the top of each column.

Materials

- Color Tiles (at least 6 of each color per pair)
- Graphing Grid (BLM 10; 1 per pair)
- crayons (an assortment per pair)
- paper (1 sheet per pair)

1. Have children place one Color Tile that corresponds to each fruit (red for apple; yellow for banana; blue for blueberry; and green for pear) above each fruit on their tally charts. Ask children to think about which fruit they like best.

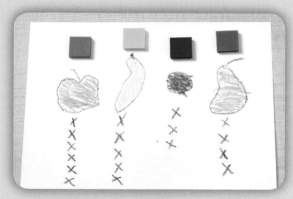

2. Ask children to stand up one at a time and say which fruit they like best. Choices are apple, banana, blueberry, or pear. Then have children make an *X* on the tally chart for each response.

⚠ Look Out!

Make sure children understand that each response is represented by one *X* on the tally sheet, and each *X* translates to one tile on the graph.

Also, watch for children who forget to include themselves in the data set.

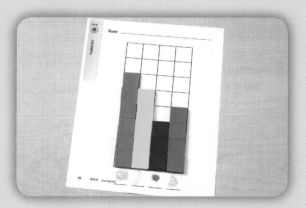

3. Have children draw pictures or place tiles on the lines below the four columns on the Graphing Grid (BLM 10) to represent the fruit. Then instruct children to graph the data on the grid using the corresponding color of tiles, with red representing apple, yellow banana, blue blueberry, and green pear.

Data Analysis and Probability

Using a Bar Graph

Informal experiences involving comparing can provide the mathematical framework for developing children's understanding of data and data analysis. In this activity, children will gather data about classroom objects, make a bar graph of the data, and then use the graph to answer questions.

Try It! *Perform the Try It! activity on the next page.*

Objective

Use information from a bar graph to make decisions.

Skills

- Counting
- Graphing data
- Interpreting data

NCTM Expectations

Data Analysis and Probability
- Pose questions and gather data about themselves and their surroundings.
- Sort and classify objects according to their attributes and organize data about the objects.
- Represent data using concrete objects, pictures, and graphs.
- Describe parts of the data and the set of data as a whole to determine what the data show.

Number and Operations
- Count with understanding and recognize "how many" in sets of objects.
- Develop understanding of the relative position and magnitude of whole numbers and of ordinal and cardinal numbers and their connections.

Talk About It

Discuss the Try It! activity.

- Have children look at their completed graphs.
- **Ask:** *Which bar is the longest? Which is the shortest?*
- **Ask:** *Which pet did the most children want to get? Which pet did the fewest children want to get? How can you tell?*
- **Ask:** *Why is it useful to make graphs?* Lead children to verbalize that graphs organize information so that it can be read quickly and easily.

Solve It

With children, reread the problem. Then have children verbally explain how they used a graph to make the decision.

More Ideas

For other ways to teach about data collection and graphing—

- Use the 4 × 12 Grid Side of the Reversible Graph It! Mat. Label four rows: red, yellow, green, blue. Distribute one crayon (red, yellow, green, or blue) to each child. Have children come up one at a time and place the crayon on the graphing mat in the appropriate row. Then ask children how they can use the graph to figure out if there is more of one kind of crayon without counting. Emphasize how to read the horizontal graph versus the vertical.
- Give each child an assortment of Pattern Blocks (4 different shapes) and ask them to sort the blocks by color or shape. Then ask children to create a graph to show which block they have the most of.

Standardized Practice

Have children try the following problem.

Some children in Jacob's class wanted to play softball. Some children wanted to play football. The class decided to make a graph to show how many children wanted to do each sport. Which sport did more children want to play? Circle the ball.

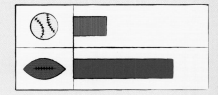

Try It! 30 minutes | Pairs

Here is a problem about data collection and graphing.

Mr. Miller's class is going to get a class pet. Mr. Miller says they can get a mouse, a frog, a fish, or a turtle. Each child will say which pet he or she wants to get. Then the class will make a graph of how many children want each pet. The class will get the pet that has the longest bar on the graph. Five children want a turtle, two want a frog, four want a fish, and seven want a mouse. Which pet will the class get?

Introduce the problem. Then have children do the activity to solve the problem. Distribute Color Tiles, Graphing Grids (BLM 10), and crayons to children.

Materials
- Color Tiles (10 of each color per pair)
- Graphing Grid (BLM 10; 1 per pair)
- crayons (an assortment per pair)

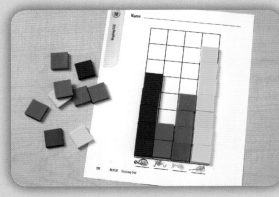

1. Have children use tiles to make a graph of the information in the problem on the Graphing Grid. They should label the bars by drawing pictures of the different animals and pick one color of tile to represent each animal.

2. Direct children to remove the tiles and to color one box on the Graphing Grid for each animal.

3. Have children look at the bars on the graph to decide which is longest. Encourage children to simply look at the bars to recognize and compare which is longest versus always counting the boxes.

⚠ Look Out!

Watch for children who color in too many boxes for a given object. Suggest that they remove the tiles and color the boxes one at a time. Also help children to understand that bar graphs can be organized vertically and horizontally. Use graphs of the same data to show a vertical bar graph versus a horizontal bar graph.

Data Analysis and Probability

Cube Tallies

Probability is the chance that something might happen. In kindergarten, children's experiences with probability should be informal, mostly taking the form of simple discussions about the likelihood of events.

Try It! *Perform the Try It! activity on the next page.*

Objective

Perform a probability experiment and make tally marks to represent data.

Skills

- Counting
- Recording data
- Making predictions

NCTM Expectations

Data Analysis and Probability
- Discuss events related to students' experiences as likely or unlikely.

Number and Operations
- Count with understanding and recognize "how many" in sets of objects.
- Develop understanding of the relative position and magnitude of whole numbers and of ordinal and cardinal numbers and their connections.

Talk About It

Discuss the Try It! activity.

- **Say:** *Now let's look at what everyone predicted. Some people thought that the red 1" Color Cube would be pulled most often from the bag, and other people thought that it would be the blue cube.*

- Discuss the concept of probability. Explain to children that because there were only two possible colors to pull from the bag, the cube had to be either red or blue. Because there were more red cubes in the bag, it was more likely that red would be drawn. Discuss how this would change if there were 5 blue and 5 red cubes in the bag. Guide children to the conclusion that if there were the same number of red cubes and blue cubes, there would be an equal chance to pick both colors.

- Compare the data of several groups. **Ask:** *How many times was the red cube pulled? How many times was the blue cube pulled?* **Say:** *Let's count.*

Solve It

With children, reread the problem. Have children draw and color the crayon they think Becca *most likely* pulled from her desk. Then have them explain why they think the color was chosen.

More Ideas

For other ways to teach about probability—

- Have children perform a similar activity using 6 yellow Link 'N' Learn® Links and 3 orange Links. Before children perform the experiment, have them predict the results.

- Give children bags with different numbers of different colors (same size) of Three Bear Family® Counters. Have children guess the number of each color of Bear, and then pull Bears and record their results. Then have them look in the bag to check their guesses.

Standardized Practice

Have children try the following problem.

Which snack do you think will be pulled from the bag without looking? Circle the piece that you think will be pulled out.

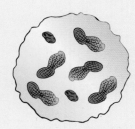

Try it! 30 minutes | Pairs

Here is a problem involving probability.

Becca had five red crayons and one blue crayon in her desk. Mr. Acres, her teacher, asked the children to take out one crayon. Without looking, Becca quickly pulled out a crayon. Which crayon do you think Becca pulled from her desk?

Introduce the problem. Then have children do the activity to solve the problem.

Distribute 1" Color Cubes and paper bags to each pair of children.

Materials
- 1" Color Cubes (5 red and 1 blue per pair)
- paper bags (1 per pair)
- paper (1 sheet per pair)
- red and blue crayons (1 per pair)

1. Display five red cubes and one blue cube. Place the cubes in a paper bag. Ask children which color they think they would pick most often from the bag without looking. Record children's predictions.

2. Now ask children to try the experiment. Have them take turns picking a cube from the bag without looking and making tally marks on a sheet of paper to record the data. Do not group the marks in fives. Have children continue for a total of ten times, returning the cube to the bag each time after recording.

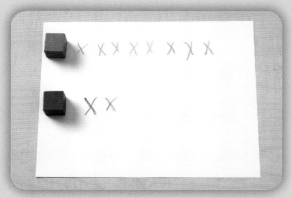

3. Help children examine their tally charts and compare their results to their predictions.

⚠ Look Out!

Watch for children who predict blue will be chosen more than red just because of color preference. Conclude that because there are far more red cubes than blue cubes in the bag, red should be chosen more often. If the activity results produce more blue than red, discuss that what is "most likely" to occur does not *always* mean it will occur, and repeat the exercise a few times to gain data in line with the natural probability of the activity.

Objective

Participate in a probability experiment and make tally marks in a table to collect data.

Skills

• Counting
• Collecting data
• Graphing

NCTM Expectations

Data Analysis and Probability
• Discuss events related to students' experiences as likely or unlikely.

Number and Operations
• Count with understanding and recognize "how many" in sets of objects.
• Develop understanding of the relative position and magnitude of whole numbers and of ordinal and cardinal numbers and their connections.

Data Analysis and Probability

Spinner Probabilities

Probability is the measure of how likely an event is. An *event* is one or more outcomes of an experiment. An *outcome* is the result of a single trial. It is important to represent data collected from an experiment in a way that makes it easy to analyze. One way to represent the data is to create a graph.

Try It! *Perform the Try It! activity on the next page.*

Talk About It

Discuss the Try It! activity.

■ Direct children to the results for the first spinner. **Say:** *Let's look at what everyone predicted. Some people said the spinner would land on blue the most, some said red, some said green, and some said yellow.* **Ask:** *Who was right?*

■ Have children look at the first spinner again. Guide children to understand that, because the spinner sections were the same size, each color had the same chance—an equal chance—of being landed on.

■ **Say:** *Now let's look at our graphs.* **Ask:** *Does your graph show equal numbers of colors?*

■ Repeat the discussion for the second spinner. Have children compare the results they got from both spinners. Conclude that because the sections were not equal the chance of the spinner landing on a color will not be equal. **Ask:** *Which color is most likely? Least likely?*

Solve It

With children, reread the problem. Have children draw and color two spinners: one spinner that gives each table an equal chance to get snacks first, and one that gives the blue table the best chance to get snacks first.

More Ideas

For other ways to teach about probability—

■ Help children create four-section spinners labeled with 4 different Backyard Bugs™. Ask children to predict the probability of spinning different Bugs. Then have children spin their spinners ten times, record the results, and make a Bug pictograph of the results. Next have them create a spinner that helps their favorite bug "win."

■ Challenge children to make a spinner with 6 equal spaces—one for each color of Link 'N' Learn® Links. Then have them make a spinner that gives their favorite color Link a better chance of being spun. Children can use their favorite color Link in place of the paper clip to make the spinner.

Standardized Practice

Have children try the following problem.

Put an X in the color the spinner is more likely to land on when spun.

Try it! 30 minutes | Pairs

Here is a problem involving probability.

Mrs. Gilmore's room has one green, one red, one blue, and one yellow table where children sit. Mrs. Gilmore has a spinner with green, red, blue, and yellow areas on it. The areas are all the same size. Mrs. Gilmore spins the spinner to decide which table gets snacks first. Jacob wanted to sit at the blue table because he said it gets snacks first more than the other tables. Is Jacob right?

Introduce the problem. Then have children do the activity to solve the problem. Distribute materials to children. Have children color the four-color spinner blue, red, green, and yellow. Show children how to make and spin a spinner by twirling a paper clip around a pencil point in the center of the spinner.

Materials
- Color Tiles (10 of each color per pair)
- Graphing Grid (BLM 10; 1 per pair)
- Spinner Pattern (BLM 11; 2 per pair)
- pencils and paper clips (1 of each per pair)

1. Ask: *If we spin the spinner once, which color do you think it will land on? What if we spin it several times? Which color do you think it will land on the most? Record children's predictions.*

2. Have children take turns spinning the spinner and placing tiles on the Graphing Grid until each child has had six turns. **Ask:** *Which color did the spinner land on the most? The least? Were any colors landed on an equal number of times?*

3. Have children color the second spinner 2 parts green, 1 part red, and 1 part yellow. Repeat the activity in order to show children that if the sections are not equal, the chances of the spinner landing on the different colors will not be equal.

⚠ Look Out!

Spinning only 12 times may not produce equal results even if the sections of the spinner are of equal size. In this case, you may wish to combine pair's results or have children repeat the activity a few times and tally the results on the board so that children can see that the makeup of the spinner really does affect the probability of landing on a given color.

Number Cards

Name _____

✂

0	
1	2
3	4
5	6
7	8
9	10

Name _____

1.

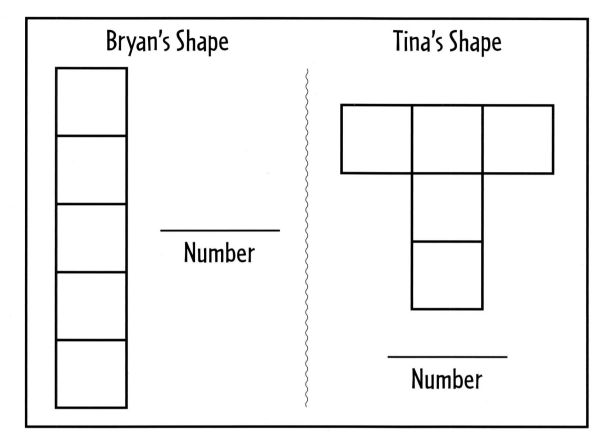

Bryan's Shape   Tina's Shape

_____
Number

_____
Number

2.

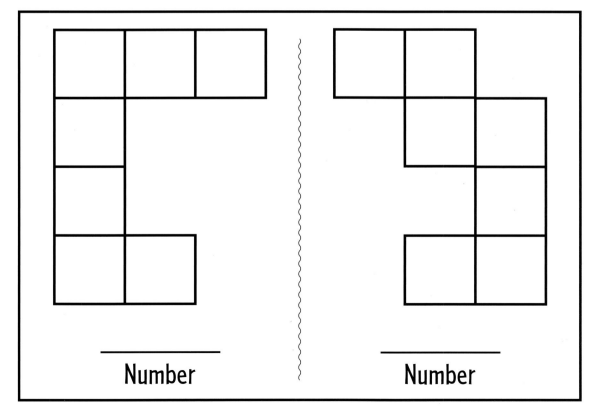

_____
Number

_____
Number

Name _____

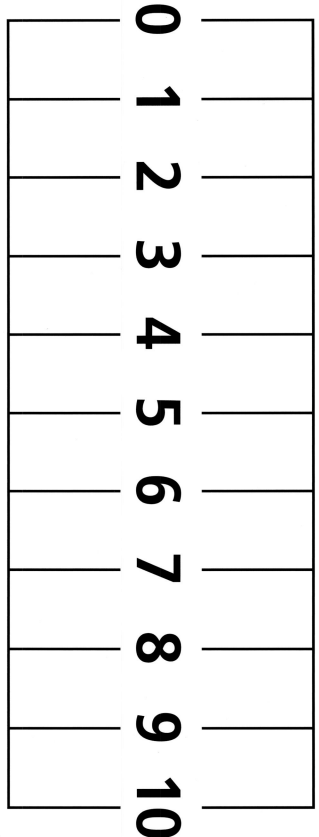

Name _____

Take-Away Workmat

Name _____

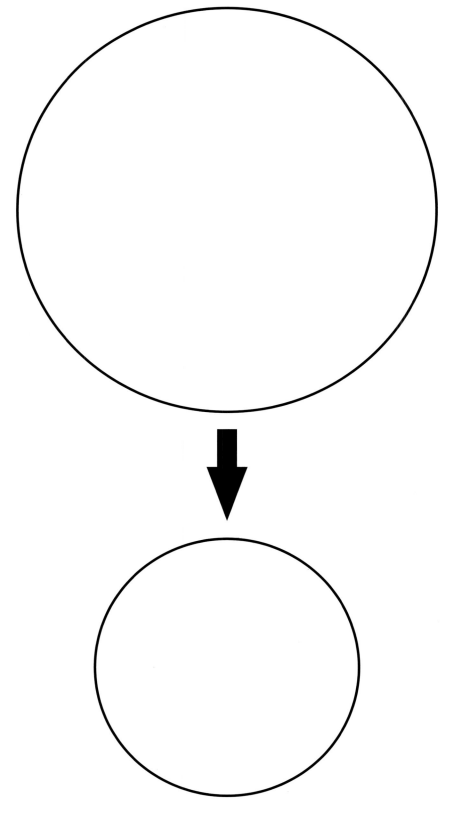

Name _____

Whole	Half

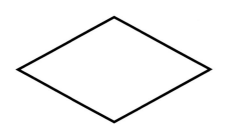

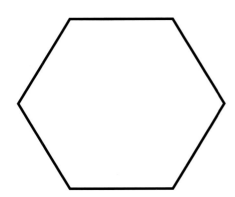

Name _____

Name _____

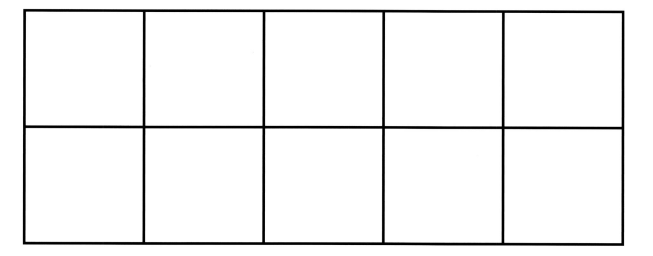

Name _____

Area 1

Area 2

Name _____

____ ____   ____   ____   ____

Spinner Pattern

Name _____

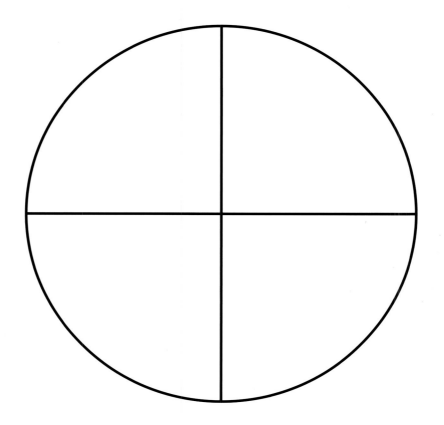

Glossary of Manipulatives

	Attribute Blocks The Attribute Blocks set includes five basic shapes (triangle, square, rectangle, circle, and hexagon) displaying different attributes. The basic shapes come in three different colors, two different sizes, and two different thicknesses. Attribute Blocks can be used to teach sorting, patterns, and identifying attributes.
	Backyard Bugs™ The set of Backyard Bugs contains counters in six different shapes (grasshopper, bumblebee, beetle, spider, dragonfly, and caterpillar) and six colors. Bugs can be used for sorting and counting activities.
	1" Color Cubes These multicolored 1" cubes can be used to teach sorting, counting, and understanding patterns. They are also ideal for introducing young children to measurement of length, width, area, and volume.
	Color Tiles 1" square tiles come in four different colors. They can be used to explore many mathematical concepts, including geometry, patterns, and number sense.
	Link 'N' Learn® Links Multicolored Links are large and easy for children to interlock. Link chains can be used to explore concepts such as number sense and operations. Use Links to teach counting, addition, and subtraction. Links can also be used to explore measuring with nonstandard units.
	Pattern Blocks Blocks include six shapes in six different colors: yellow hexagon, red trapezoid, orange square, green triangle, blue parallelogram, and tan rhombus. Each side length is calibrated so that pieces fit together. They can be used to teach concepts from all strands of mathematics. Blocks illustrate algebraic concepts such as patterning and sorting. Children learn geometry and measurement concepts such as symmetry, transformations, and area. Blocks can also be used to show number concepts such as counting and fractions.

Reversible Graph It! Mat

This graphing mat has a Venn diagram on one side. On the other side it has a 4 × 12 square grid that can be used for graphing. Both sides are ideal for activities that use manipulatives or other real objects. The mat can be used to introduce graphing data. It can also be used for activities such as sorting and classifying geometric shapes.

Snap Cubes®

Each side of a Snap Cube can be connected to another Cube. Cubes can be used to teach a variety of different math concepts. Use Cubes to explore number sense and operations with activities involving counting, place value, addition, and subtraction. Or use Cubes to show measuring using nonstandard units. Cubes can also be used to demonstrate patterning and basic geometry.

Sorting Circles

These collapsible circles can be used to teach beginning algebraic thinking by having children sort objects into sets. They can also be used for classifying geometric shapes by attribute.

Three Bear Family® Counters

Bear Counters come in three different sizes and weights—Baby Bear™ (4 grams), Mama Bear™ (8 grams), and Papa Bear™ (12 grams). Bear Counters can be used to teach abstract concepts involving number sense and operations by allowing children to act them out. Use Bears to explore sorting and comparing sets, counting, estimating, addition and subtraction, and sequencing. Bears can be used to experiment with measuring mass, or to teach patterning concepts and early algebra.

Index

Boldface page numbers indicate when a manipulative is used in the Try It! activity.